WILDFLOWERS

A Book of Days

Paintings by LILIAN SNELLING

The Royal Horticultural Society

FRANCES LINCOLN

Frances Lincoln Limited
4 Torriano Mews, Torriano Avenue,
London NW5 2RZ

Wildflowers: A Book of Days

Profits from the sale of this book are an important contribution to the funds raised by the Royal Horticultural Society, a registered charity.

British Library Cataloguing-in-publication data.
A catalogue record for this book is available from the British Library.

ISBN 0-7112-1380-1

Printed in Hong Kong

First Frances Lincoln Edition 1999

LILIAN SNELLING
1879-1972

'Her work as a botanical artist is without living peer [and] as a botanical illustrator and technician her work materially eclipses that of Redouté,' wrote the distinguished botanist Dr George Lawrence, on hearing of the death of Lilian Snelling.

Lilian Snelling was born in St Mary Cray in Kent to a well-known family of millers, who at one time owned the local brewery. The youngest of the family, she spent most of her life in St Mary Cray, living with her three other unmarried sisters in Spring Hall, the family home. The drawings in this volume are her earliest surviving work: we are seeing her at the very beginning of her career. Most of the locations noted here are the fields and hedgerows of Kent around St Mary Cray and nearby Tunbridge Wells. The earliest drawing is dated 22 May 1900, and the last 27 July 1905, but the majority were painted in 1900 and 1901. The composite pictures, which formed the sketchbook she kept in her early twenties, were not completed at single sittings; often, she would return to a partially finished drawing and add further plants. Most of the plants are British wild flowers; a few are garden varieties.

After studying art and lithography at the Royal College of Art in London, she worked as the protegée of the arboriculturist and plant hunter Henry John Elwes (1846-1922), painting plants that grew in his garden at Colesbourne in Gloucestershire. (When Arthur Grove published two supplements to Elwes' *Monograph of the Genus Lilium*, 1933-1940, it was to Lilian Snelling that he turned for the magnificent illustrations, which are regarded as her masterpiece.)

From 1916 to 1921 Lilian Snelling worked at the Royal Botanic Garden, Edinburgh, under the guidance of the Keeper, Sir Isaac Bayley Balfour, and it was there that she developed the meticulous style that was to stand her in such good stead on *Curtis's Botanical Magazine*, which had been purchased by the Royal Horticultural Society in 1921.

In 1922 she was hired as the magazine's principal illustrator and lithographer and, over a period of thirty years, she made over 740 plates, an achievement that put her at the forefront of her art. Volume 169 was dedicated to her, with praise for her 'remarkable delicacy of accurate outlines, brilliancy of colour and intricate gradation of tone'. Lilian Snelling retired from the *Botanical Magazine* in 1952. She was awarded the MBE in 1954 and the Victoria Medal of Honour, the Royal Horticultural Society's highest award, in 1955. The last of the sisters to survive, she died at the age of ninety-three.

The flowering of Lilian Snelling's mature style formed the outstanding model for the British botanical artists of the last half-century. The drawings in this volume, show a little-known phase of her career, giving the opportunity to see her talent in the bud.

Brent Elliott
The Royal Horticultural Society

January

1

2

3

4

5

6

7

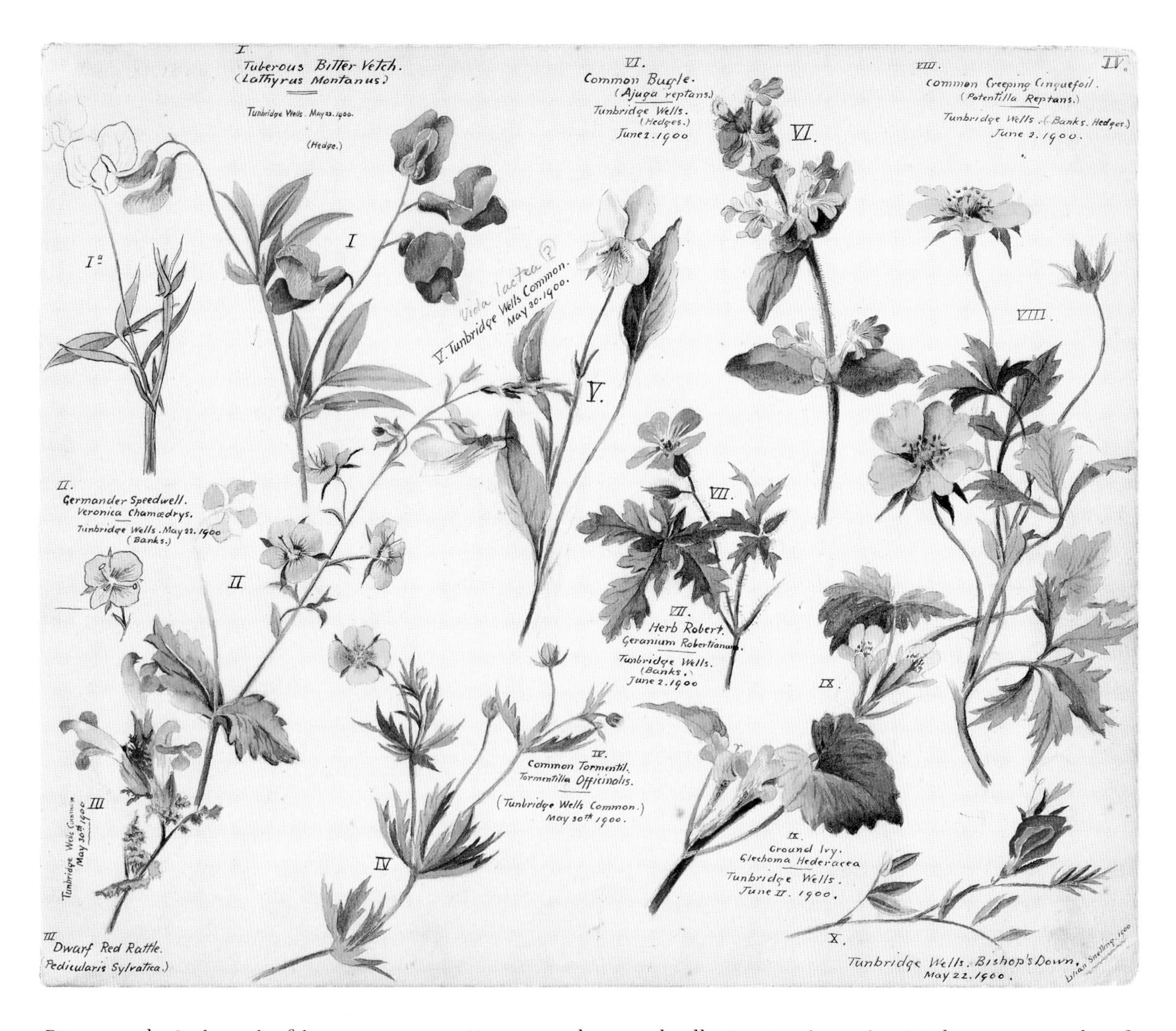
I.
Tuberous Bitter Vetch.
(Lathyrus Montanus.)
Tunbridge Wells. May 23. 1900.
(Hedge.)
VI.
Common Bugle.
(Ajuga reptans.)
Tunbridge Wells.
(Hedges.)
June 2. 1900
VIII.
Common Creeping Cinquefoil.
(Potentilla Reptans.)
Tunbridge Wells. (Banks. Hedges.)
June 2. 1900.
IV.
Iª
I
Viola lactea ?
V. Tunbridge Wells Common.
May 30. 1900.
VI.
VIII.
V.
II.
Germander Speedwell.
Veronica Chamædrys.
Tunbridge Wells. May 22. 1900
(Banks.)
II
VII.
VII.
Herb Robert.
Geranium Robertianum.
Tunbridge Wells.
(Banks.)
June 2. 1900
IX.
IV.
Common Tormentil.
Tormentilla Officinalis.
(Tunbridge Wells Common.)
May 30th 1900.
III
Tunbridge Wells Common
May 30th 1900
IV
IX.
Ground Ivy.
Glechoma Hederacea
Tunbridge Wells.
June 11. 1900.
X.
III
Dwarf Red Rattle.
(Pedicularis Sylvatica.)
Tunbridge Wells. Bishop's Down.
May 22. 1900.
Lilian Snelling 1900

Bitter vetch, *Lathyrus linifolius* var.*montanus* (I); germander speedwell, *Veronica chamaedrys* (II); lousewort or dwarf red rattle, *Pedicularis sylvatica* (III); tormentil, *Potentilla erecta* (IV); pale dog violet, *Viola lactea* (V); bugle, *Ajuga reptans* (VI); herb Robert, *Geranium robertianum* (VII); creeping cinquefoil, *Potentilla reptans* (VIII); ground ivy, *Glechoma hederacea* (IX); and common vetch, *Vicia sativa* (X)

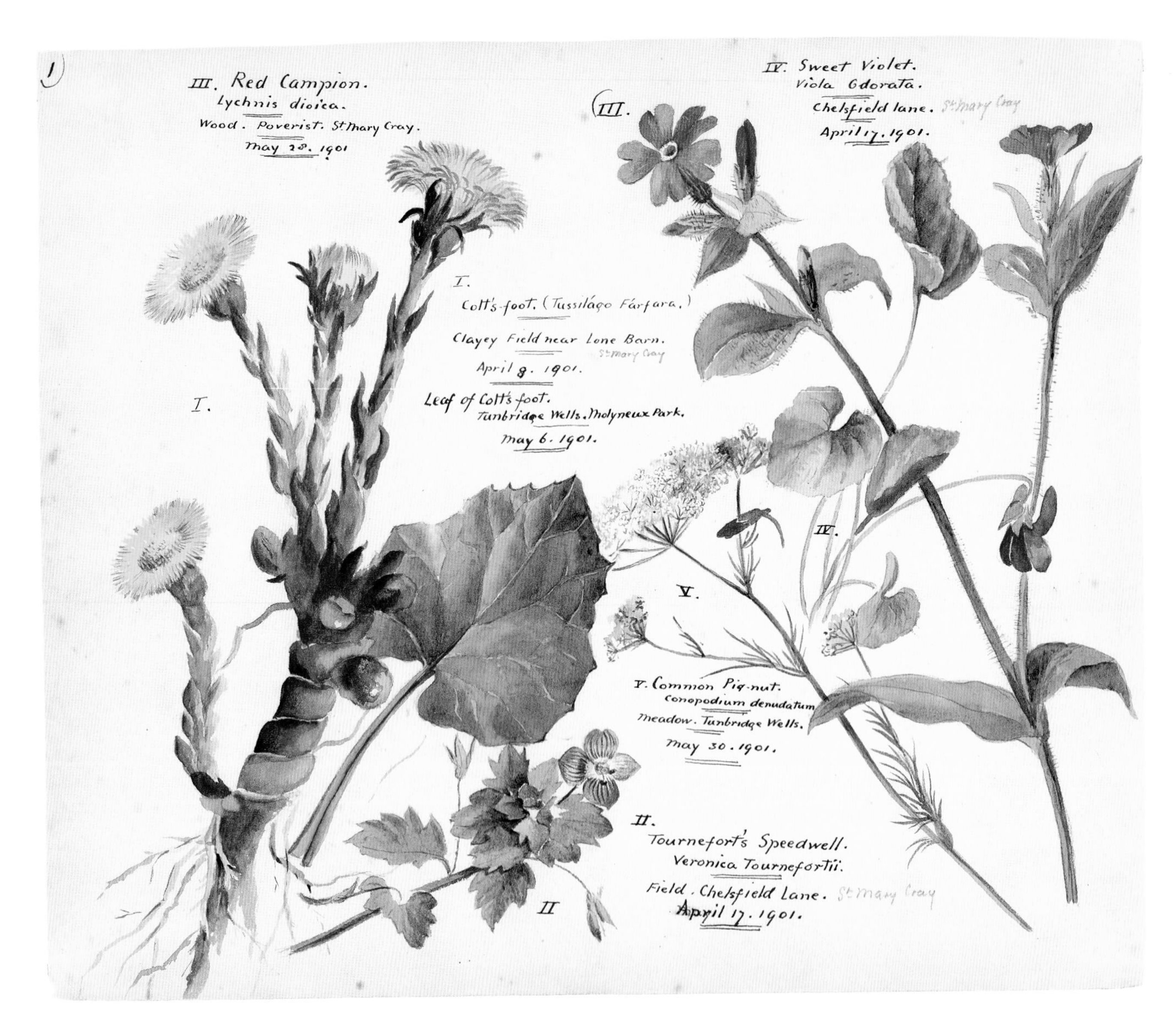
1
III. Red Campion.
Lychnis dioica.
Wood. Poverist. St Mary Cray.
May 28. 1901
IV. Sweet Violet.
Viola Odorata.
Chelsfield lane. St Mary Cray
April 17. 1901.
III.
I.
Colt's-foot. (Tussilágo Fárfara.)
Clayey Field near Lone Barn.
St Mary Cray
April 8. 1901.
Leaf of Colt's foot.
Tunbridge Wells. Molyneux Park.
May 6. 1901.
I.
IV.
V.
V. Common Pig-nut.
Conopodium denudatum
Meadow. Tunbridge Wells.
May 30. 1901.
II.
Tourneforts Speedwell.
Veronica Tournefortii.
Field. Chelsfield Lane. St Mary Cray
April 17. 1901.
II

Coltsfoot, *Tussilago farfara* (I); common field speedwell, *Veronica persica* (II); red campion, *Silene dioica* (III); sweet violet, *Viola odorata* (IV); and pignut, *Conopodium majus* (V)

8

9

10

11

January

12

13

14

January

15

16

17

18

19

20

21

January

22

23

24

25

26

27

28

January
February

29

30

31

1

2

3

4

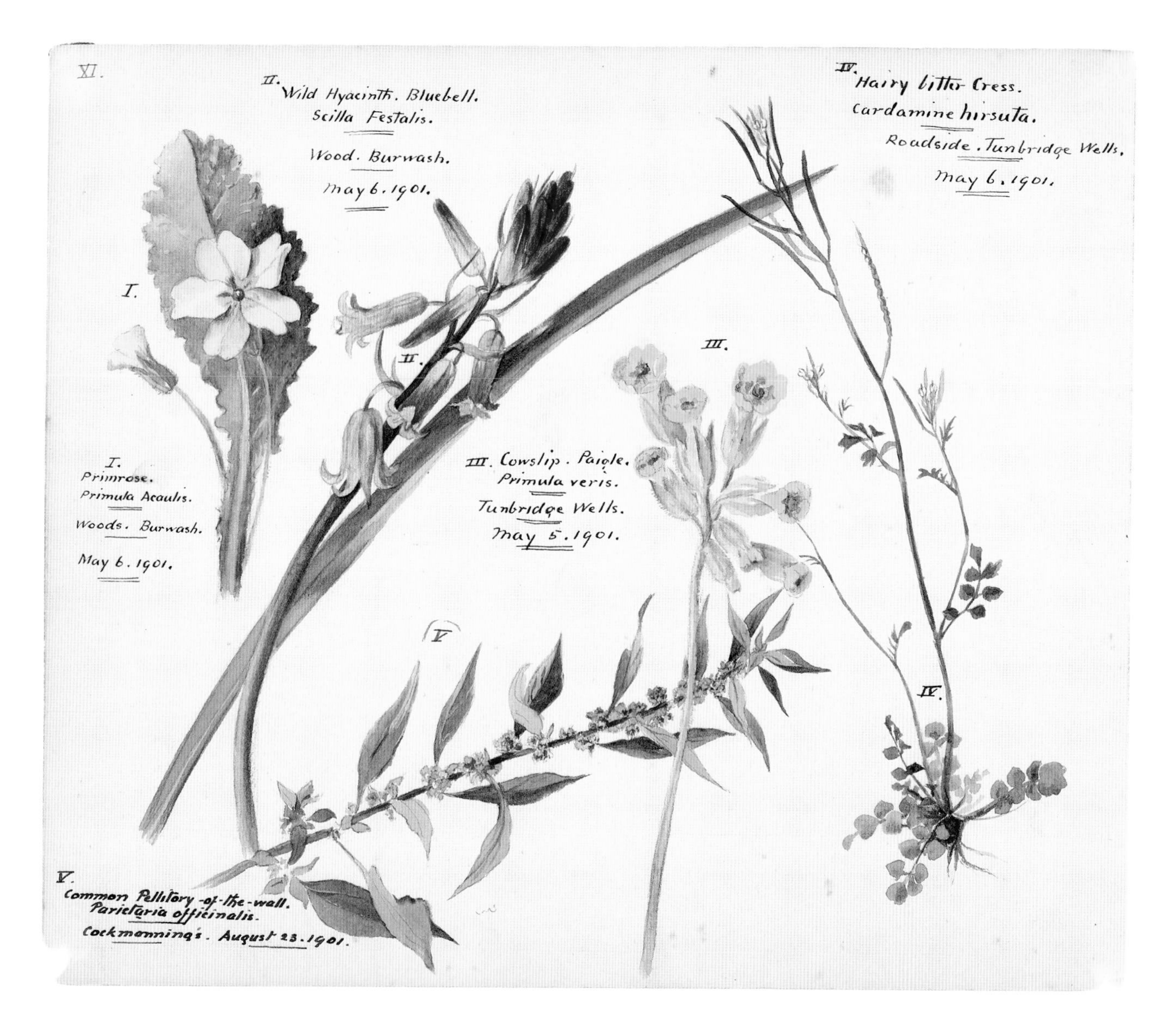
XI.
II. Wild Hyacinth. Bluebell.
Scilla Festalis.
Wood. Burwash.
May 6. 1901.
IV. Hairy bitter Cress.
Cardamine hirsuta.
Roadside. Tunbridge Wells.
May 6. 1901.
I.
II.
III.
I.
Primrose.
Primula Acaulis.
Woods. Burwash.
May 6. 1901.
III. Cowslip. Paigle.
Primula veris.
Tunbridge Wells.
May 5. 1901.
V
IV.
V.
Common Pellitory-of-the-wall.
Parietaria officinalis.
Cockmannings. August 23. 1901.

Primrose, *Primula vulgaris* (I); a pinkish form of bluebell, *Hyacinthoides non-scripta* (II); cowslip, *Primula veris* (III); hairy bittercress, *Cardamine hirsuta* (IV); and pellitory of the wall, *Parietaria judaica* (V)

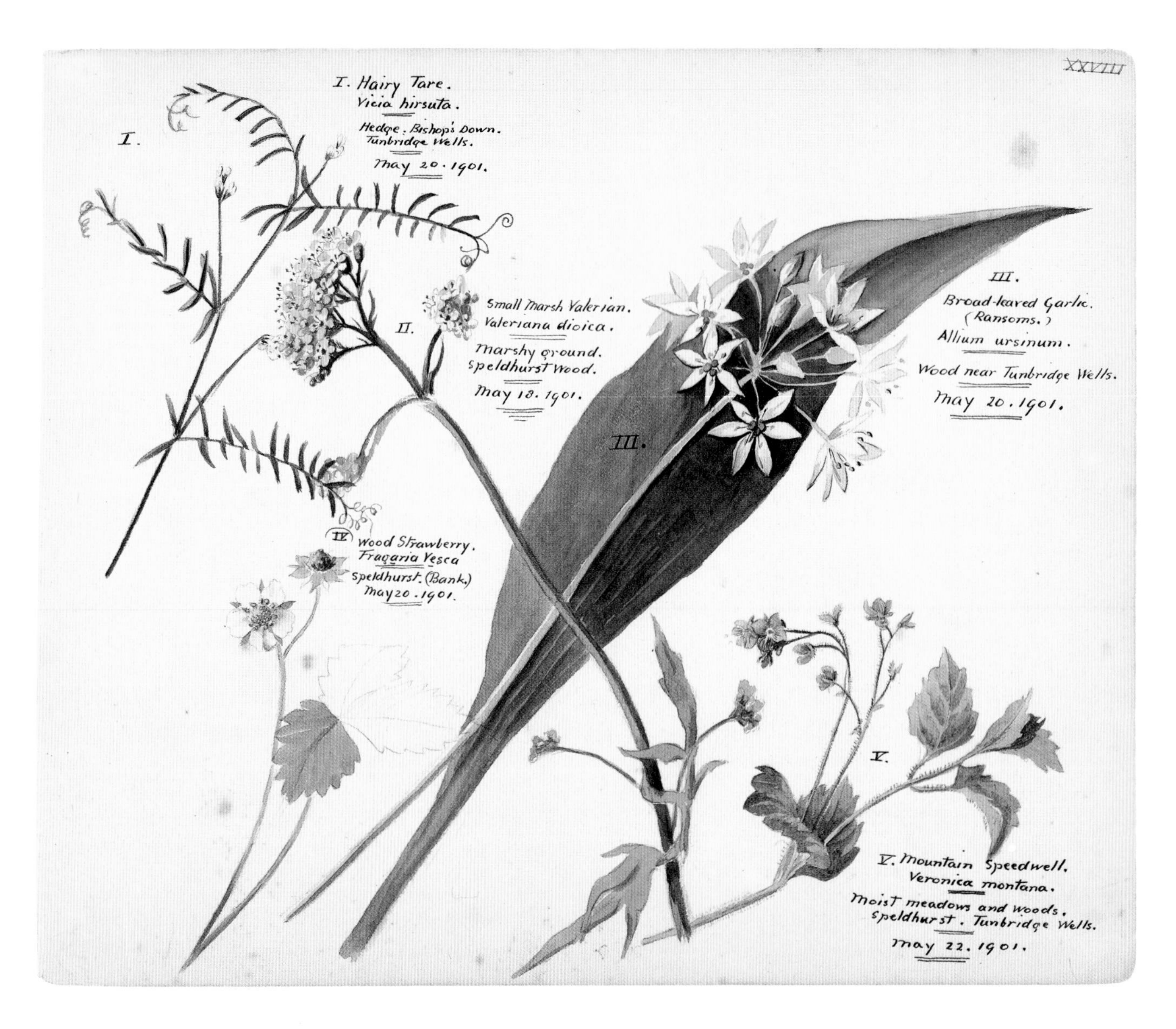
XXVIII
I. Hairy Tare.
Vicia hirsuta.
Hedge: Bishop's Down.
Tunbridge Wells.
May 20. 1901.
I.
Small Marsh Valerian.
Valeriana dioica.
Marshy ground.
Speldhurst Wood.
May 18. 1901.
II.
III.
Broad-leaved Garlic.
(Ransoms.)
Allium ursinum.
Wood near Tunbridge Wells.
May 20. 1901.
III.
IV Wood Strawberry.
Fragaria Vesca
Speldhurst. (Bank.)
May 20. 1901.
V.
V. Mountain Speedwell.
Veronica montana.
Moist meadows and woods.
Speldhurst. Tunbridge Wells.
May 22. 1901.

Hairy tare, *Vicia hirsuta* (I); common valerian, *Valeriana officinalis* (II); ramsons or wild garlic, *Allium ursinum* (III); wild strawberry, *Fragaria vesca* (IV); and wood speedwell, *Veronica montana* (V)

5

6

7

8

February

9

10

11

February

12

13

14

15

16

17

18

19

20

21

22

February

23

24

25

February
March

26

27

28

29

1

2

3

XVI.
I. Field Wood-Rush.
Juncoides Campêstre.
May. 10. 1901.
Pasture.
Tunbridge Wells.
I.
II. Yellow Dead-nettle, Weasel-snout, Archangel.
Lamium Galeóbdolun.
Speldhurst Wood.
May 15. 1901.
III. Large-flowered Bitter-Cress.
Cardamine amara.
Tunbridge Wells.
Riverside near Hurst Wood.
June 5. 1901.
III)
II.
V.
IV.
IV.
Common Sainfoin, Cock's-head.
Onobrychis viciæfolia.
Ramsgate. June 11. 1901.
V.
Ox-eye Daisy. Chrysanthemum Leucanthemum.
Tunbridge Wells. Meadows.
June 26. 1901.

Field wood-rush, *Luzula campestris* (I); yellow archangel, *Lamium galeobdolon* (II); large bittercress, *Cardamine amara* (III); sainfoin, *Onobrychis viciifolia* (IV); and ox-eye daisy, *Leucanthemum vulgare* (V)

XXX
I.
Mealy Guelder Rose. Wayfaring Tree.
Viburnum lantana.
May 20. 1901.
St Mary Cray
II. Lesser Spearwort.
Ranunculus Flammula.
Moist Meadow.
Speldhurst. Tun. Wells.
June 1. 1901.
IV.
Ground Thistle.
Cnicus acaulis.
Chalky meadow near East Hall.
August 6. 1901.
II.
I.
III.
IV.
III.
Common Yellow Cow-wheat.
Melampyrum Pratense.
Hurst Wood.
Tunbridge Wells.
June 1. 1901.

Wayfaring tree, *Viburnum lantana* (I); lesser spearwort, *Ranunculus flammula* (II); common cow-wheat, *Malampyrum pratense* (III); and dwarf or ground thistle, *Cirsium acaule* (IV)

4

March

5

8

6

9

7

10

March

11

12

13

14

15

16

17

18

19

20

21

March

22

23

24

March

25

26

27

28

29

30

31

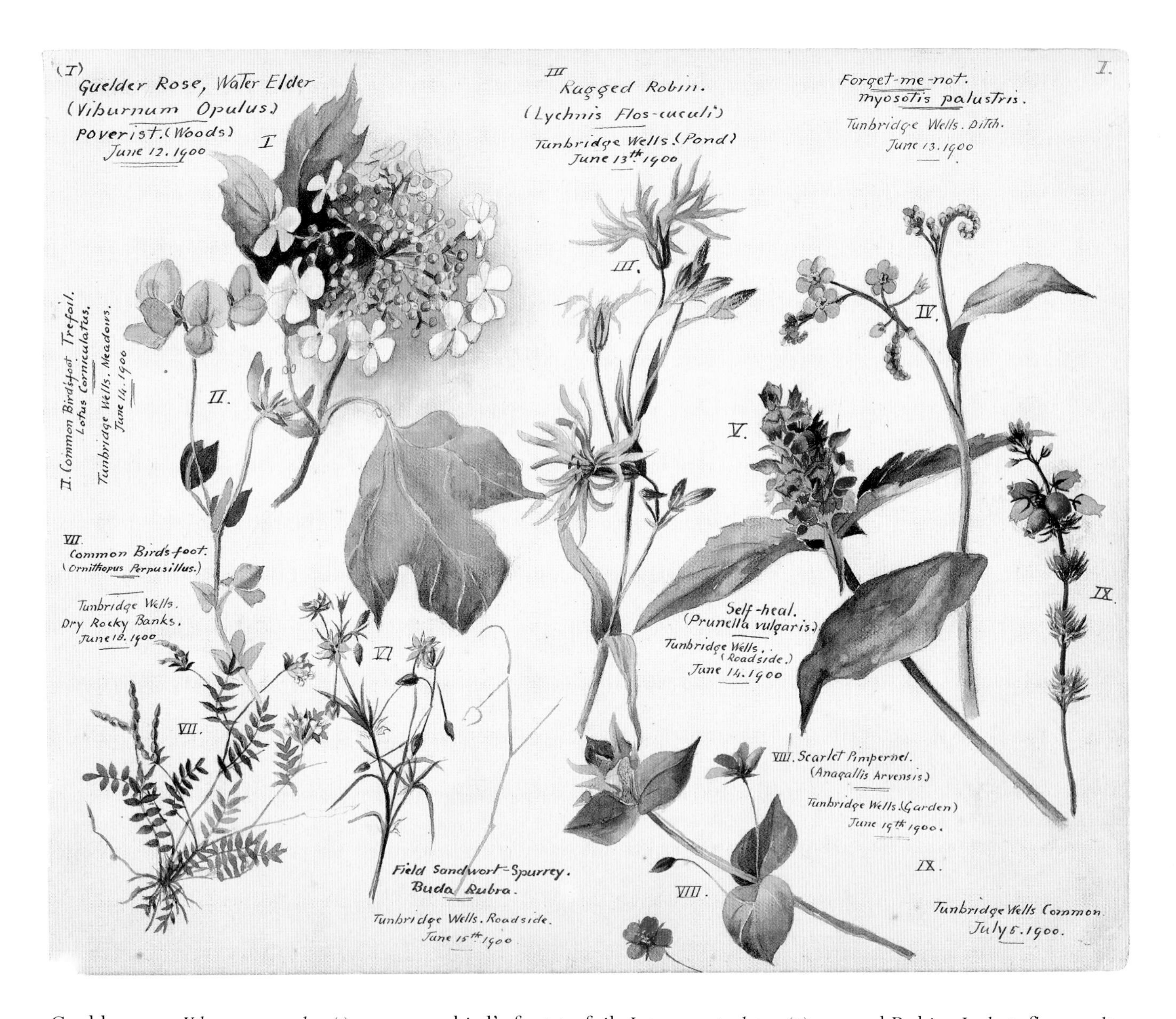
(I)
Guelder Rose, Water Elder
(Viburnum Opulus.)
Poverist. (Woods)
June 12. 1900
I
III
Ragged Robin.
(Lychnis Flos-cuculi)
Tunbridge Wells. (Pond)
June 13th 1900
Forget-me-not.
myosotis palustris.
Tunbridge Wells. Ditch.
June 13. 1900
I.
III.
IV.
II. Common Birdsfoot Trefoil.
Lotus Corniculatus.
Tunbridge Wells. Meadows.
June 14. 1900
II.
V.
VII.
Common Bird's-foot.
(Ornithopus Perpusillus.)
Tunbridge Wells.
Dry Rocky Banks.
June 18. 1900
IX.
Self-heal.
(Prunella vulgaris.)
Tunbridge Wells.
(Roadside.)
June 14. 1900
VI
VII.
VIII. Scarlet Pimpernel.
(Anagallis Arvensis.)
Tunbridge Wells. (Garden)
June 19th 1900.
IX.
Field Sandwort-Spurrey.
Buda Rubra.
VIII.
Tunbridge Wells. Roadside.
June 15th 1900
Tunbridge Wells Common.
July 5. 1900.

Guelder-rose, *Viburnum opulus* (I); common bird's-foot trefoil, *Lotus corniculatus* (II); ragged Robin, *Lychnis flos-cuculi* (III); water forget-me-not, *Myosotis scorpioides* (IV); self-heal, *Prunella vulgaris* (V); sand spurrey, *Spergularia rubra* (VI); bird's-foot, *Ornithopus perpusillus* (VII); scarlet pimpernel, *Anagallis arvensis* (VII); and bell heather, *Erica cinerea* (IX)

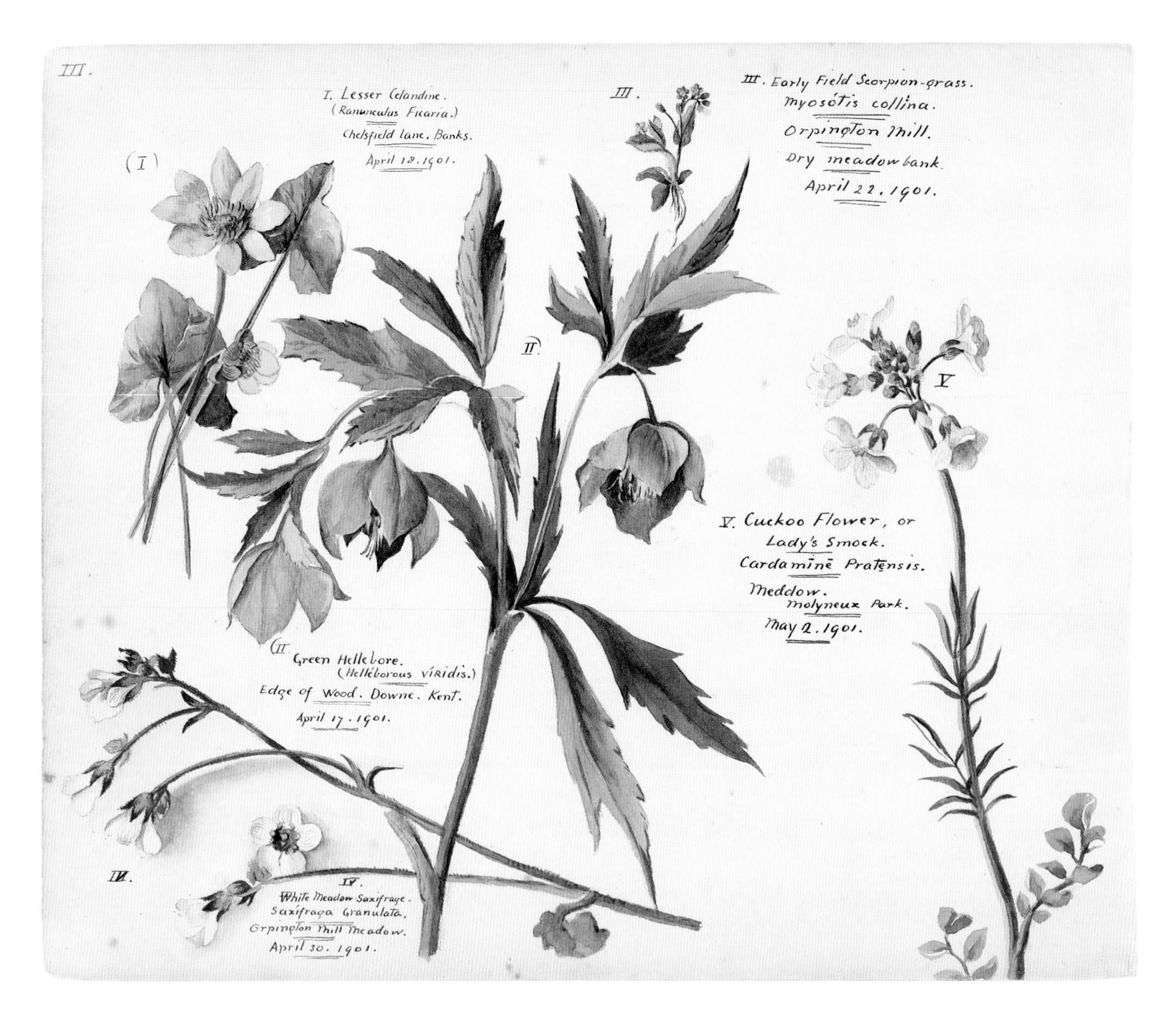
III.
I. Lesser Celandine.
(Ranunculus Ficaria.)
Chelsfield lane. Banks.
April 18. 1901.
(I)
III.
III. Early Field Scorpion-grass.
Myosótis collina.
Orpington Mill.
Dry meadow bank.
April 22. 1901.
II.
V
V. Cuckoo Flower, or
Lady's Smock.
Cardamine Pratensis.
Meddow.
Molyneux Park.
May 2. 1901.
(II. Green Hellebore.
(Helleborous viridis.)
Edge of Wood. Downe. Kent.
April 17. 1901.
IV.
IV.
White Meadow Saxifrage.
Saxifraga Granulata.
Orpington Mill meadow.
April 30. 1901.

Lesser celandine, *Ranunculus ficaria* (I); green hellebore, *Helleborus viridis* (II); early forget-me-not, *Myosotis ramosissima* (III); meadow saxifrage, *Saxifraga granulata* (IV); and cuckoo flower or lady's smock, *Cardamine pratensis* (V)

April

1

2

3

4

5

6

7

April

8

9

10

11

12

13

14

15

16

17

18

April

19

20

21

April

22

23

24

25

26

27

28

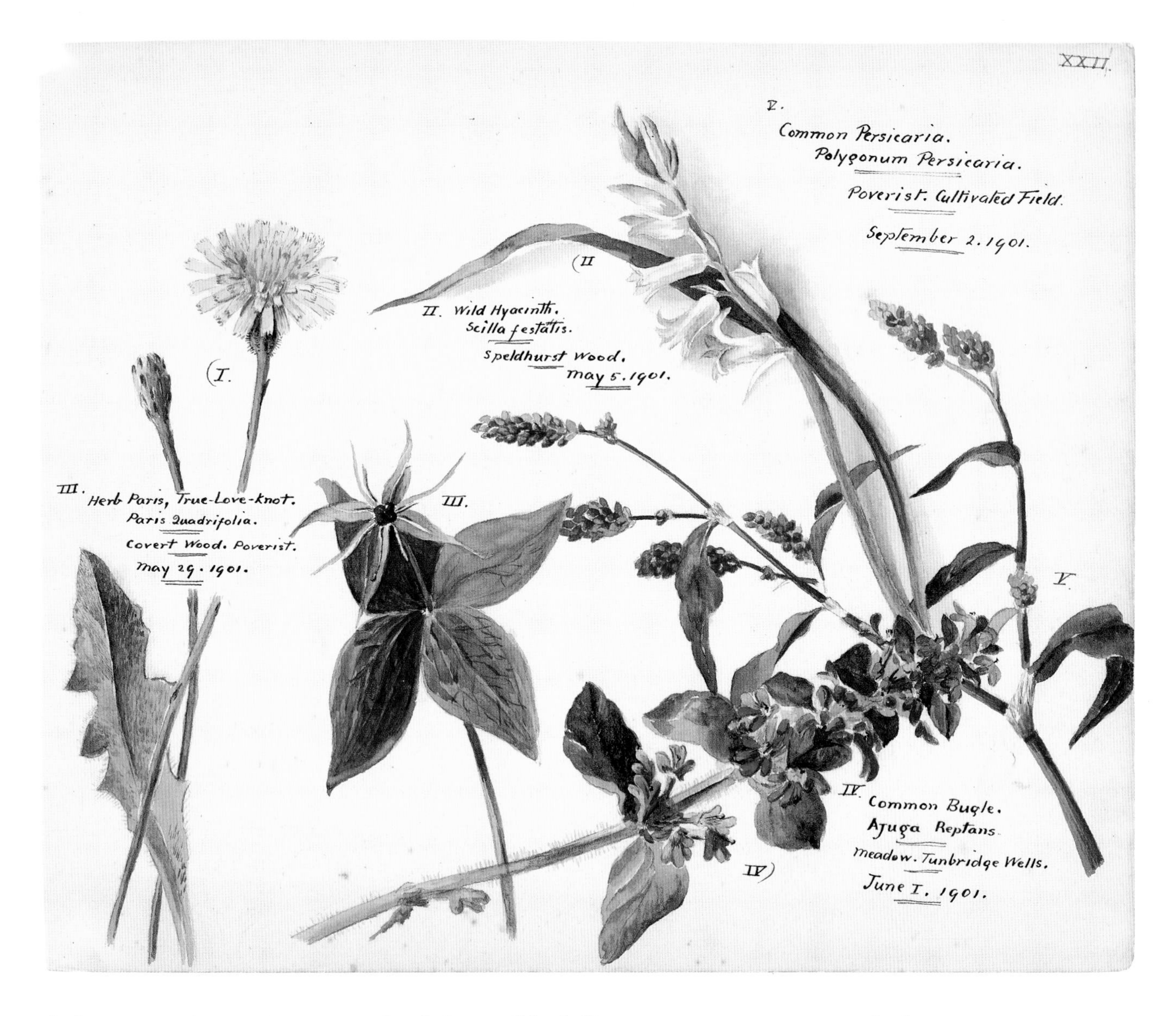
XXII.
V.
Common Persicaria.
Polygonum Persicaria.
Poverist. Cultivated Field.
September 2. 1901.
(II
II. Wild Hyacinth.
Scilla festatis.
Speldhurst Wood.
May 5. 1901.
(I.
III. Herb Paris, True-Love-knot.
Paris Quadrifolia.
Covert Wood. Poverist.
May 29. 1901.
III.
V.
IV. Common Bugle.
Ajuga Reptans.
meadow. Tunbridge Wells.
June I. 1901.
IV)

Cat's ear, *Hypochoeris radicata* (I); a whitish form of bluebell, *Hyacinthoides non-scripta* (II); herb Paris, *Paris quadrifolia* (III); bugle, *Ajuga reptans* (IV); and redshank, *Persicaria maculosa* (V)

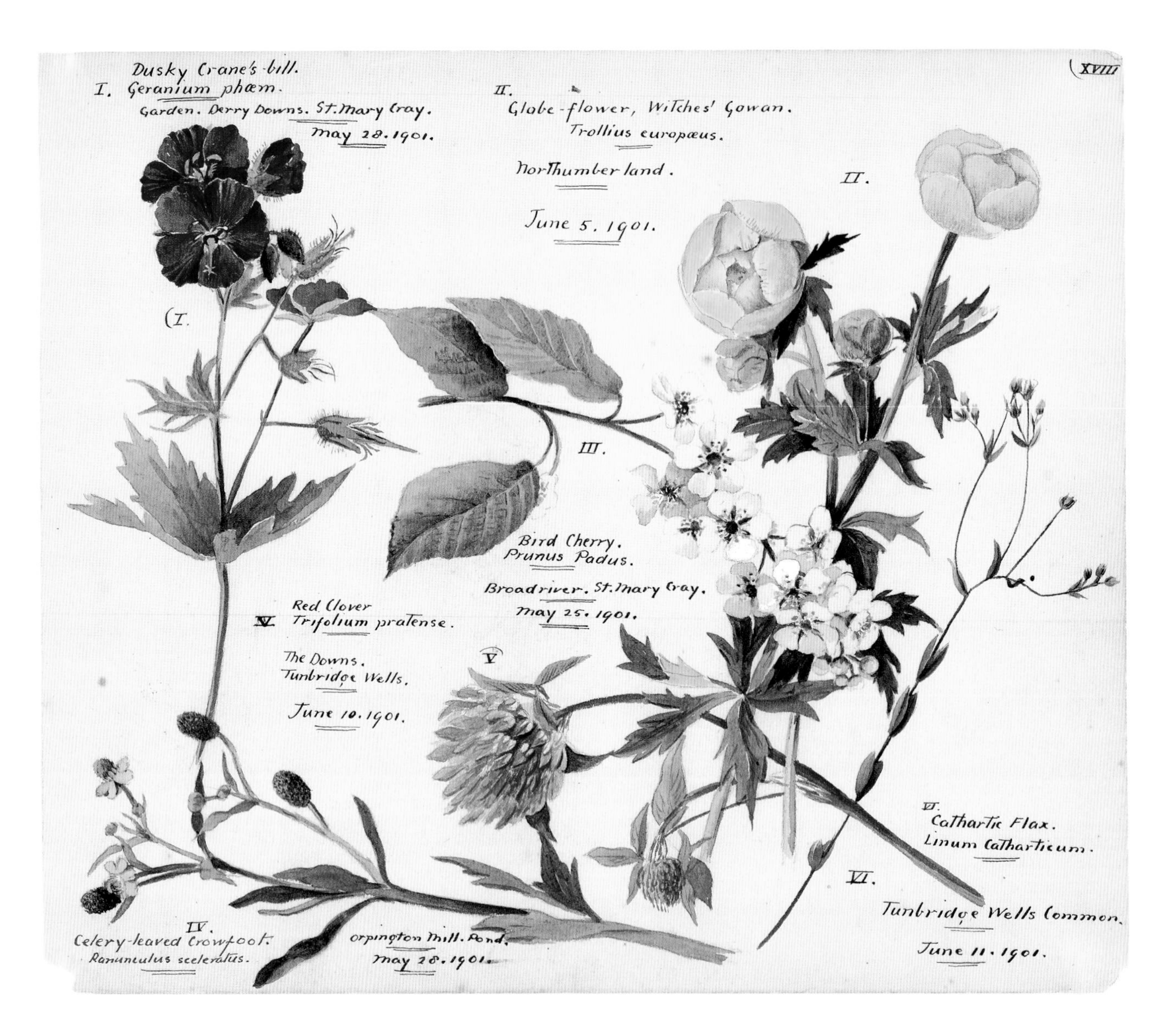
XVIII
Dusky Crane's-bill.
I. Geranium phæm.
Garden. Derry Downs. St. Mary Cray.
May 28. 1901.
II.
Globe-flower, Witches' Gowan.
Trollius europæus.
Northumberland.
June 5. 1901.
II.
(I.
III.
Bird Cherry.
Prunus Padus.
Broadriver. St. Mary Cray.
May 25. 1901.
Red Clover
V Trifolium pratense.
The Downs.
Tunbridge Wells.
June 10. 1901.
V
VI.
Cathartic Flax.
Linum Catharticum.
VI.
Tunbridge Wells Common.
June 11. 1901.
IV.
Celery-leaved Crowfoot.
Ranunculus sceleratus.
Orpington Mill. Pond.
May 28. 1901.

Dusky crane's-bill, *Geranium phaeum* (I); globeflower or witches' gowan, *Trollius europaeus* (II); bird cherry, *Prunus padus* (III); celery-leaved buttercup, *Ranunculus sceleratus* (IV); red clover, *Trifolium pratense* (V); and cathartic flax, *Linum catharticum* (VI)

29

30

1

2

April
May

3

4

5

May

6

7

8

9

10

11

12

13

14

15

16

May

17

18

19

May

20

21

22

23

24

25

26

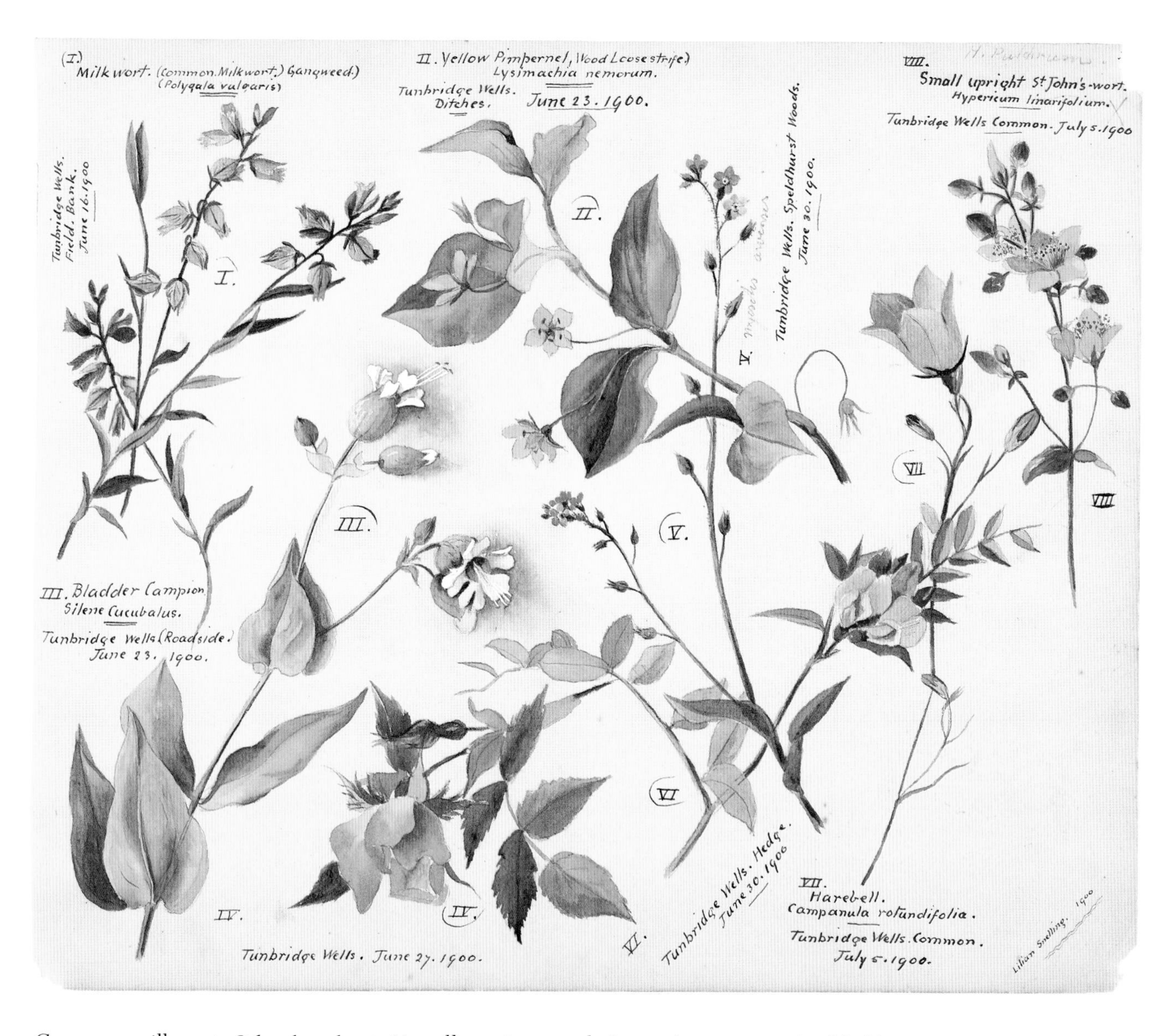
(I.) Milkwort. (Common Milkwort.) Gangweed.)
(Polygala vulgaris)
II. Yellow Pimpernel, Wood Loosestrife.)
Lysimachia nemorum.
Tunbridge Wells. Ditches. June 23. 1900.
VIII. Small upright St John's-wort.
Hyperi cum linarifolium.
Tunbridge Wells Common. July 5. 1900
Tunbridge Wells. Field. Bank. June 16. 1900
Tunbridge Wells. Speldhurst Woods. June 30. 1900.
III. Bladder Campion.
Silene Cucubalus.
Tunbridge Wells (Roadside.) June 23. 1900.
VII. Harebell.
Campanula rotundifolia.
Tunbridge Wells. Common. July 5. 1900.
Tunbridge Wells. Hedge. June 30. 1900
Tunbridge Wells. June 27. 1900.
Lilian Snelling. 1900

Common milkwort, *Polygala vulgaris* (I); yellow pimpernel, *Lysimachia nemorum* (II); bladder campion, *Silene vulgaris* (III); a form of dog rose, *Rosa canina* (IV); field forget-me-not, *Myosotis arvensis* (V); bush vetch, *Vicia sepium* (VI); harebell, *Campanula rotundifolia* (VII); and slender St. John's wort, *Hypericum pulchrum* (VIII)

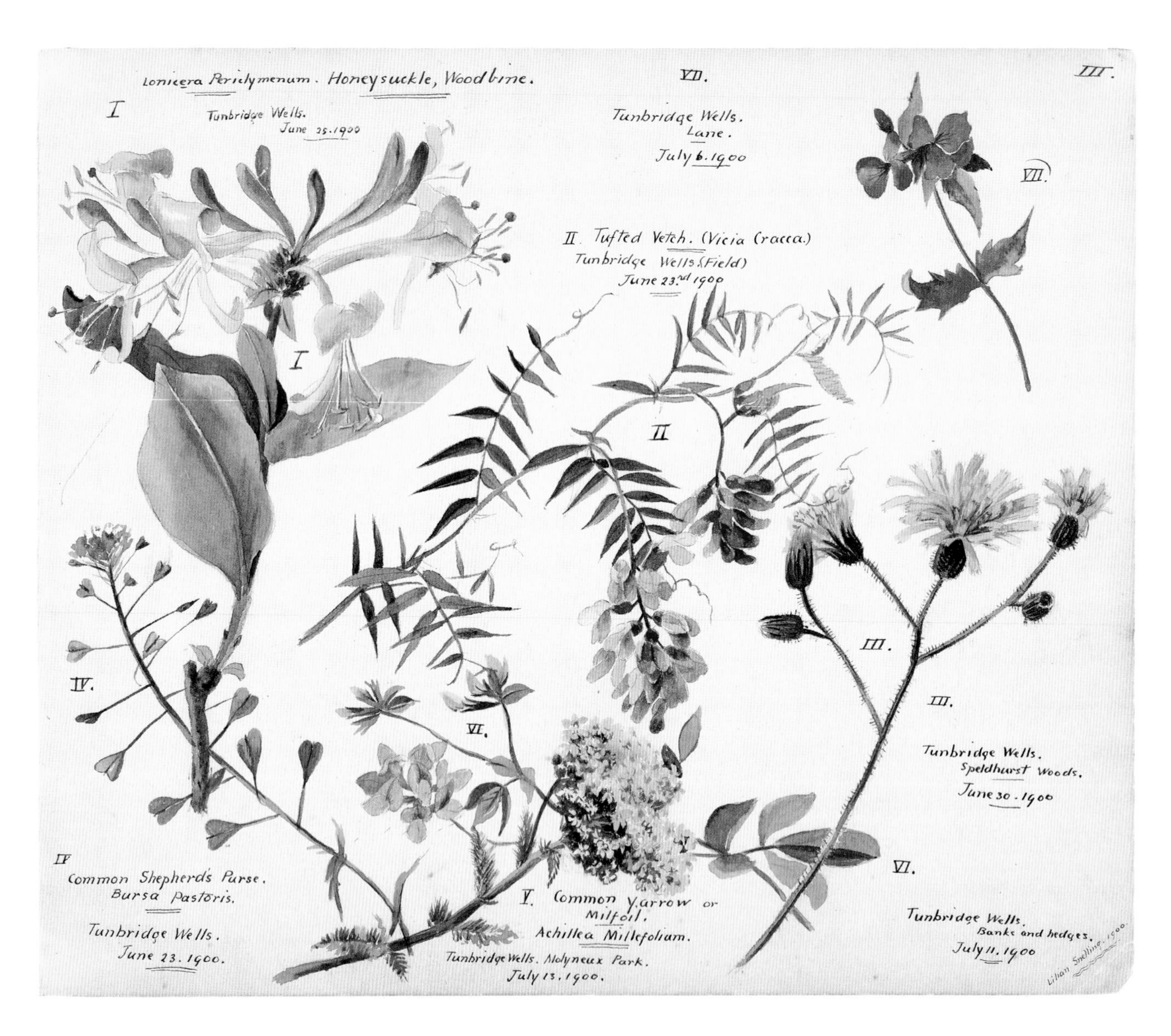
Lonicera Periclymenum. Honeysuckle, Woodbine.
I
Tunbridge Wells.
June 25.1900
VII.
Tunbridge Wells.
Lane.
July 6.1900
III.
VII.
II. Tufted Vetch. (Vicia Cracca.)
Tunbridge Wells (Field)
June 23rd 1900
I
II
IV.
III.
III.
VI.
Tunbridge Wells.
Speldhurst Woods.
June 30.1900
IV
Common Shepherd's Purse.
Bursa Pastoris.
Tunbridge Wells.
June 23.1900.
V. Common Yarrow or
Milfoil.
Achillea Millefolium.
Tunbridge Wells. Molyneux Park.
July 13.1900.
VI.
Tunbridge Wells.
Banks and hedges.
July 11.1900
Lilian Snelling. 1900.

Honeysuckle or woodbine, *Lonicera periclymenum* (I); tufted vetch, *Vicia cracca* (II); one of the hawkweeds, Hieracium sp. (III); shepherd's purse, *Capsella bursa-pastoris* (IV); yarrow or milfoil, *Achillea millefolium* (V); common bird's-foot trefoil, *Lotus corniculatus* (VI); and honesty, *Lunaria annua* (VII)

27

28

29

30

May

June

31

1

2

June

3

4

5

6

7

8

9

10

11

12

13

June

14

15

16

June

20

17

21

18

22

19

23

I. Corn Flag, Yellow Iris.
Iris Pseudacorus.
Side of stream.
Southover. Burwash.
June 17. 1901.
Gnaphalium
Cud-weed. June 29. 1901.
Tunbridge Wells.
III. Barberry.
Berberis vulgaris.
Tunbridge Wells. Hedge.
Nr Broadwater
June 19. 1901.
(1)
I.
II
III)
IV
IV. Greater Skull-cap.
Scutellaria galericulata.
Southover. Burwash
(Bank of Pond.)
July 8. 1901.
Enchanter's nightshade.
Circæa lutetiana
Orpington Mill.
August 20. 1901.

Yellow iris, *Iris pseudacorus* (I); marsh cudweed, *Gnaphalium uliginosum* (II); barberry, *Berberis vulgaris* (III); skullcap, *Scutellaria galericulata* (IV); and enchanter's nightshade, *Circaea lutetiana* (below)

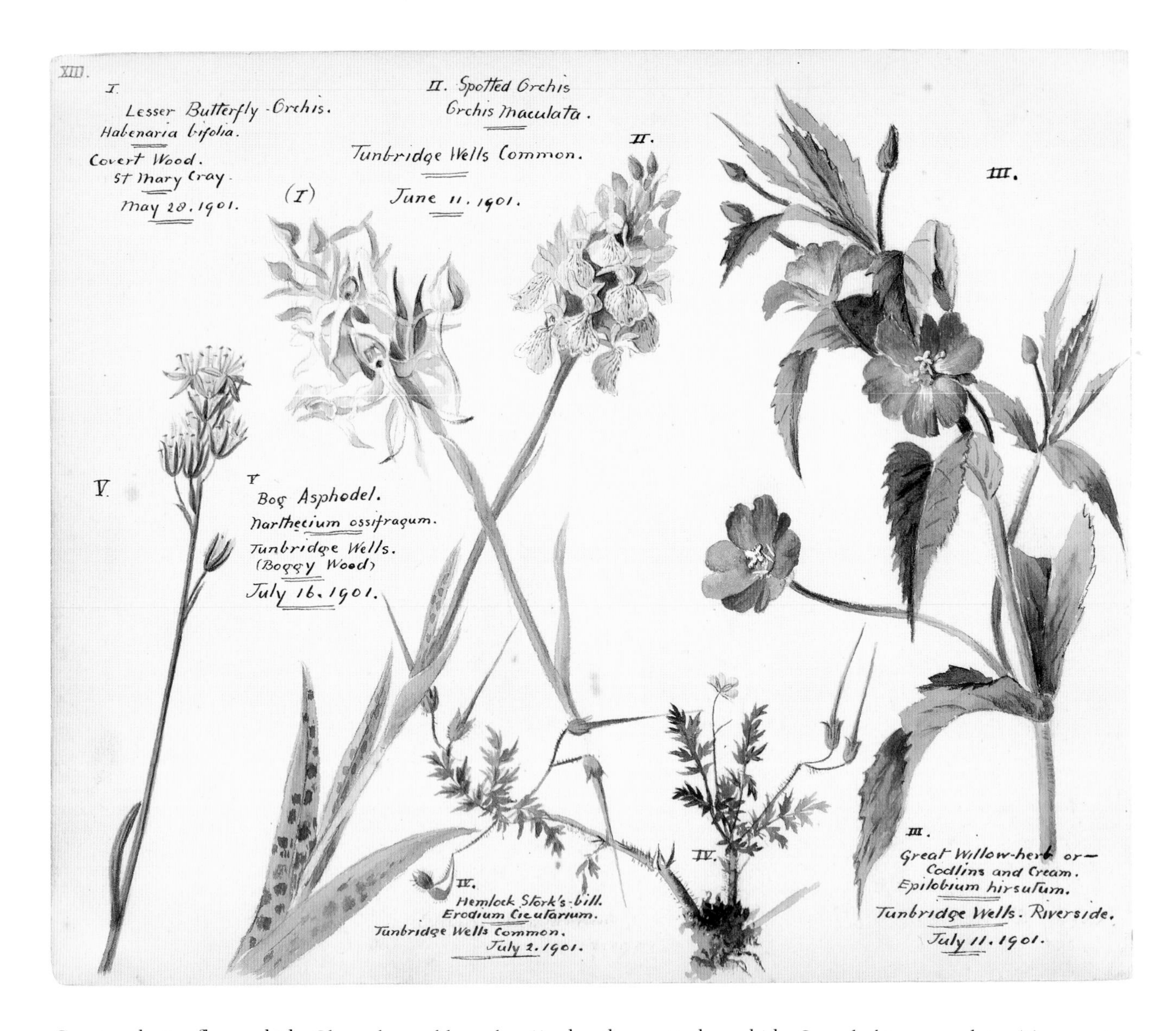
XIII.
I.
Lesser Butterfly-Orchis.
Habenaria bifolia.
Covert Wood.
St Mary Cray.
May 20. 1901.
(I)
II. Spotted Orchis
Orchis maculata.
Tunbridge Wells Common.
June 11. 1901.
II.
III.
V.
V
Bog Asphodel.
Narthecium ossifragum.
Tunbridge Wells.
(Boggy Wood)
July 16. 1901.
IV.
IV.
Hemlock Stork's-bill.
Erodium Cicutarium.
Tunbridge Wells Common.
July 2. 1901.
III.
Great Willow-herb or—
Codlins and Cream.
Epilobium hirsutum.
Tunbridge Wells. Riverside.
July 11. 1901.

Greater butterfly orchid, *Platanthera chlorantha* (I); heath spotted orchid, *Dactylorhiza maculata* (II); greater willowherb, *Epilobium hirsutum* (III); common stork's bill, *Erodium cicutarium* (IV); and bog asphodel, *Narthecium ossifragum* (V)

June

24

25

26

27

28

29

30

July

1

2

3

4

5

6

7

8

9

10

11

July

12

13

14

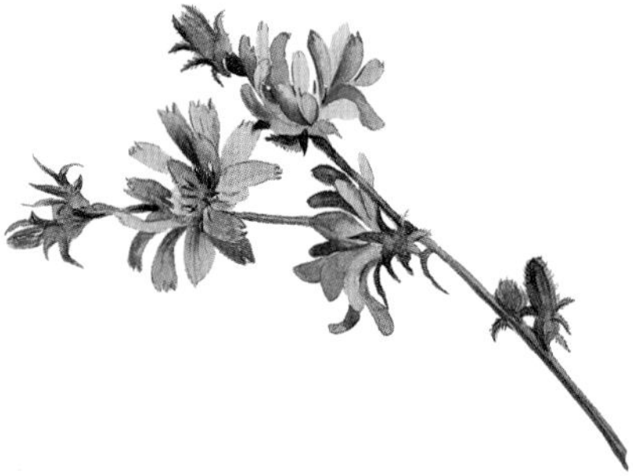

July

15

16

17

18

19

20

21

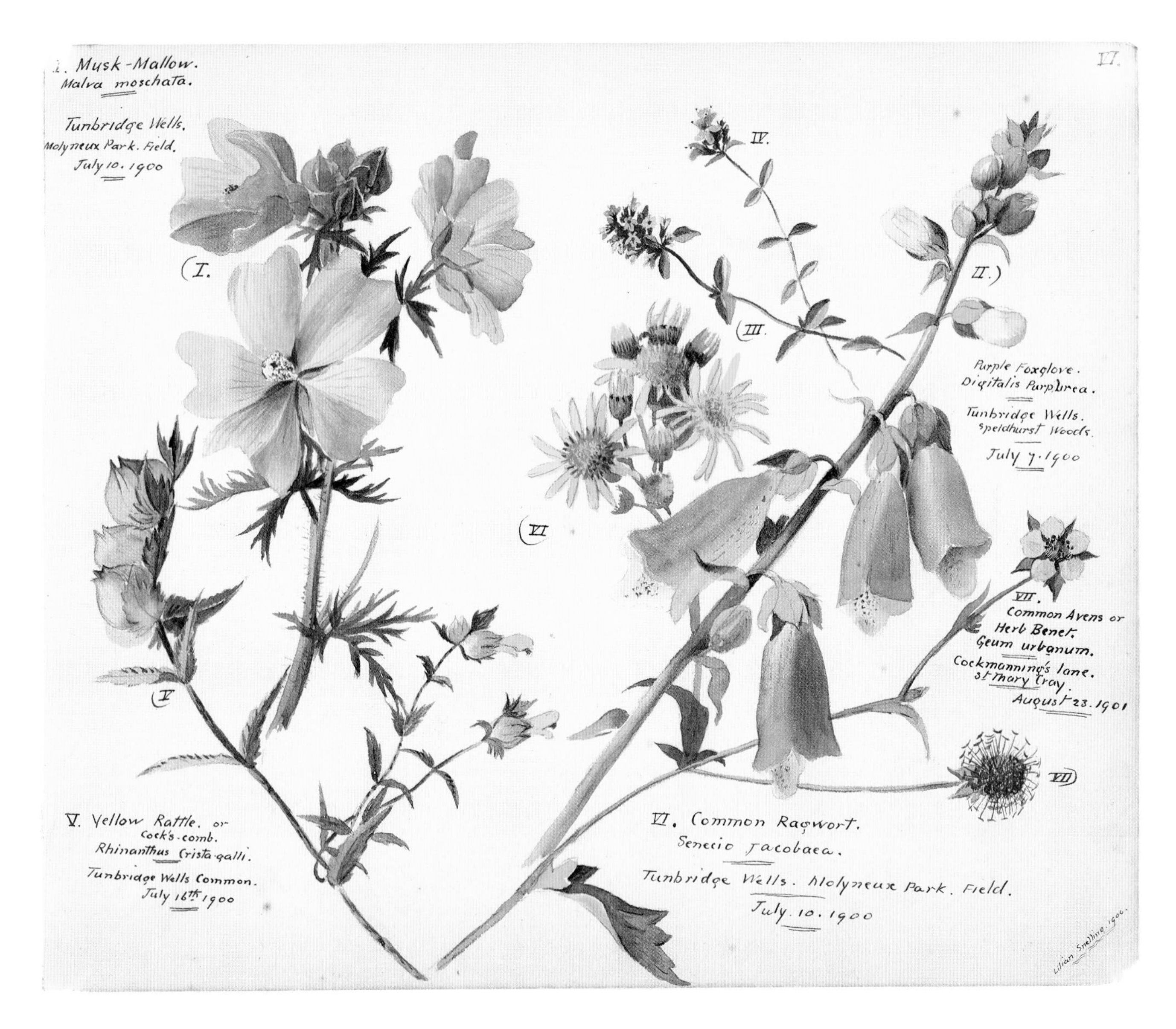
Musk-Mallow.
Malva moschata.
Tunbridge Wells.
Molyneux Park. Field.
July 10. 1900
(I.
IV.
(III.
II.)
VI
Purple Foxglove.
Digitalis Purpurea.
Tunbridge Wells.
Speldhurst Woods.
July 7. 1900
VII.
Common Avens or
Herb Benet.
Geum urbanum.
Cockmanning's lane.
St Mary Cray.
August 23. 1901
V
VII
V. Yellow Rattle. or
Cock's-comb.
Rhinanthus Crista-galli.
Tunbridge Wells Common.
July 16th 1900
VI. Common Ragwort.
Senecio Jacobaea.
Tunbridge Wells. Molyneux Park. Field.
July. 10. 1900
Lilian Snelling. 1900.

Musk mallow, *Malva moschata* (I); foxglove, *Digitalis purpurea* (II); possibly wild thyme, *Thymus praecox* ssp. *brittanicus* (III); possibly hairy thyme, *Thymus praecox* (IV); narrow-leaved rattle, *Rhinanthus angustifolius* (V); common ragwort, *Senecio jacobaea* (VI); and herb bennet, *Geum urbanum* (VII)

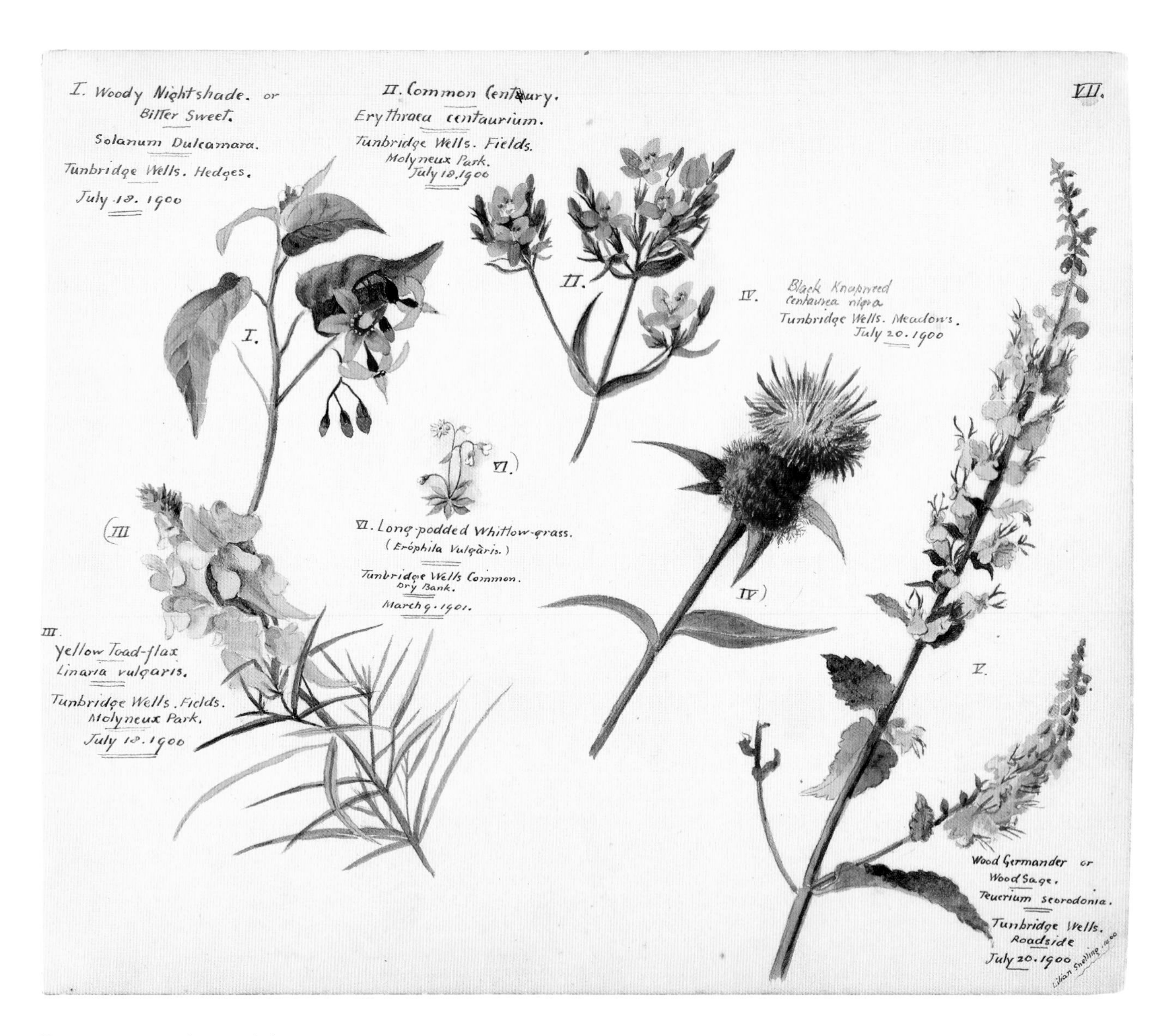
I. Woody Nightshade. or
Bitter Sweet.
Solanum Dulcamara.
Tunbridge Wells. Hedges.
July 18. 1900
II. Common Centaury.
Erythraea centaurium.
Tunbridge Wells. Fields.
Molyneux Park.
July 18. 1900
VII.
IV. Black Knapweed
Centaurea nigra
Tunbridge Wells. Meadows.
July 20. 1900
VI. Long-podded Whitlow-grass.
(Eróphila Vulgàris.)
Tunbridge Wells Common.
Dry Bank.
March 9. 1901.
III. Yellow Toad-flax
Linaria vulgaris.
Tunbridge Wells. Fields.
Molyneux Park.
July 18. 1900
Wood Germander or
Wood Sage.
Teucrium scorodonia.
Tunbridge Wells.
Roadside
July 20. 1900
Lilian Snelling 1900

Bittersweet, *Solanum dulcamara* (I); common centaury, *Centaurium erythraea* (II); common toadflax, *Linaria vulgaris* (III); common knapweed or hardheads, *Centaurea nigra* (IV); wood sage, *Teucrium scorodonia* (V); and common whitlow-grass, *Erophila verna* (VI)

22

23

24

25

July

26

27

28

July
August

29

30

31

1

2

3

4

5

August

6

9

7

10

8

11

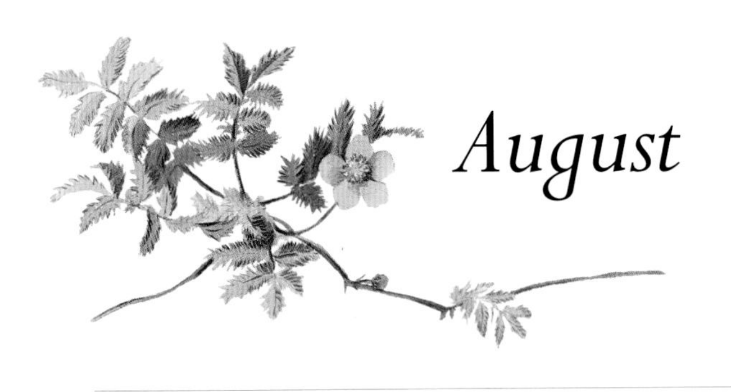

August

12

13

14

15

16

17

18

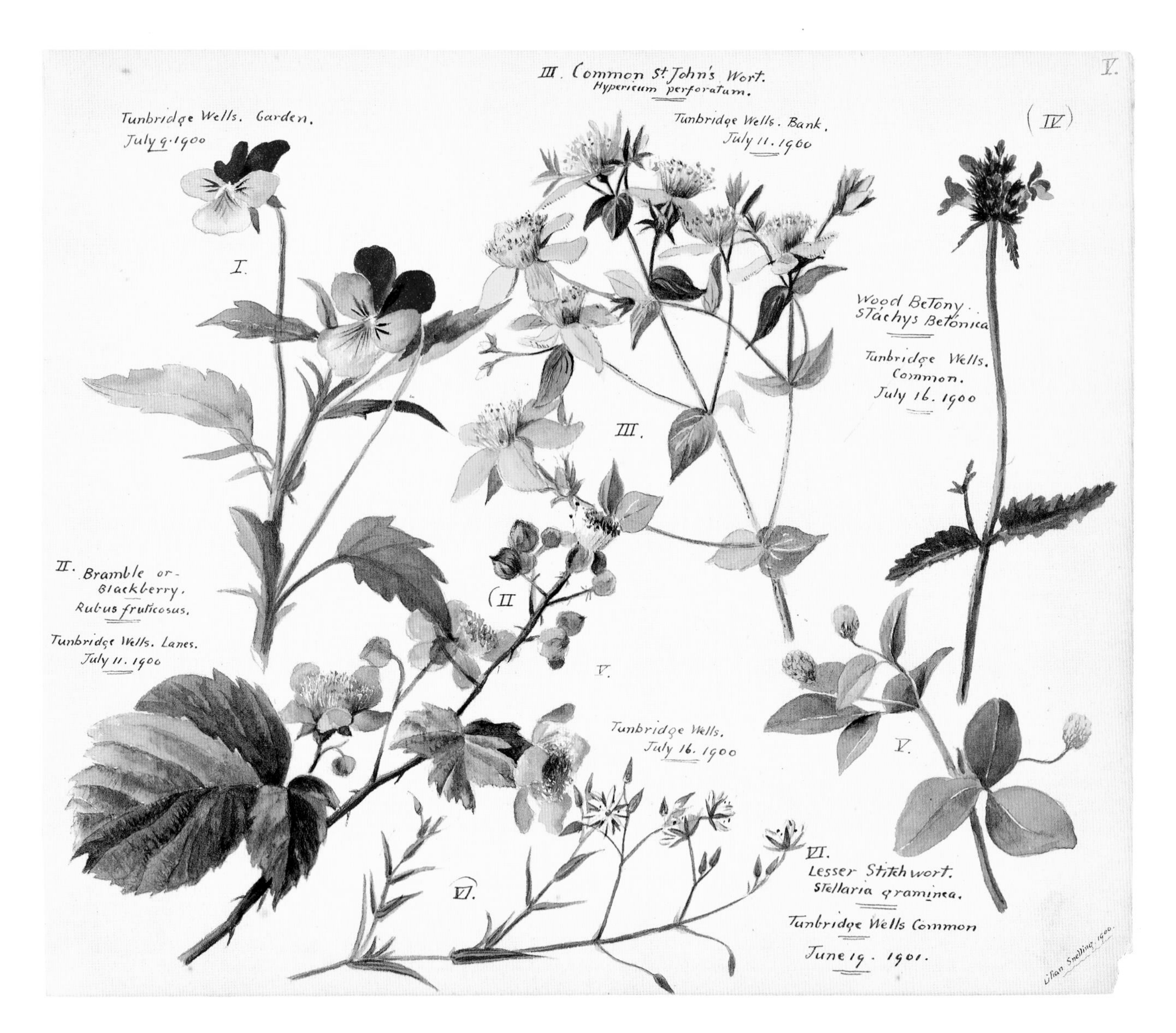
III. Common St John's Wort.
Hypericum perforatum.
V.
Tunbridge Wells. Garden.
July 9. 1900
Tunbridge Wells. Bank.
July 11. 1900
(IV)
I.
Wood Betony.
Stachys Betonica
Tunbridge Wells.
Common.
July 16. 1900
III.
II. Bramble or-
Blackberry.
Rubus fruticosus.
Tunbridge Wells. Lanes.
July 11. 1900
(II
V.
Tunbridge Wells.
July 16. 1900
V.
VI.
Lesser Stitchwort.
Stellaria graminea.
Tunbridge Wells Common
June 19. 1901.
VI.
Lilian Snelling. 1900.

Wild pansy or heartsease, *Viola tricolor* (I); bramble or blackberry, *Rubus fruticosus* (II); perforate or St. John's wort, *Hypericum perforatum* (II); wood betony, *Betonica officinalis* (IV); black medick, *Medicago lupulina* (V); and lesser stitchwort, *Stellaria graminea* (VI)

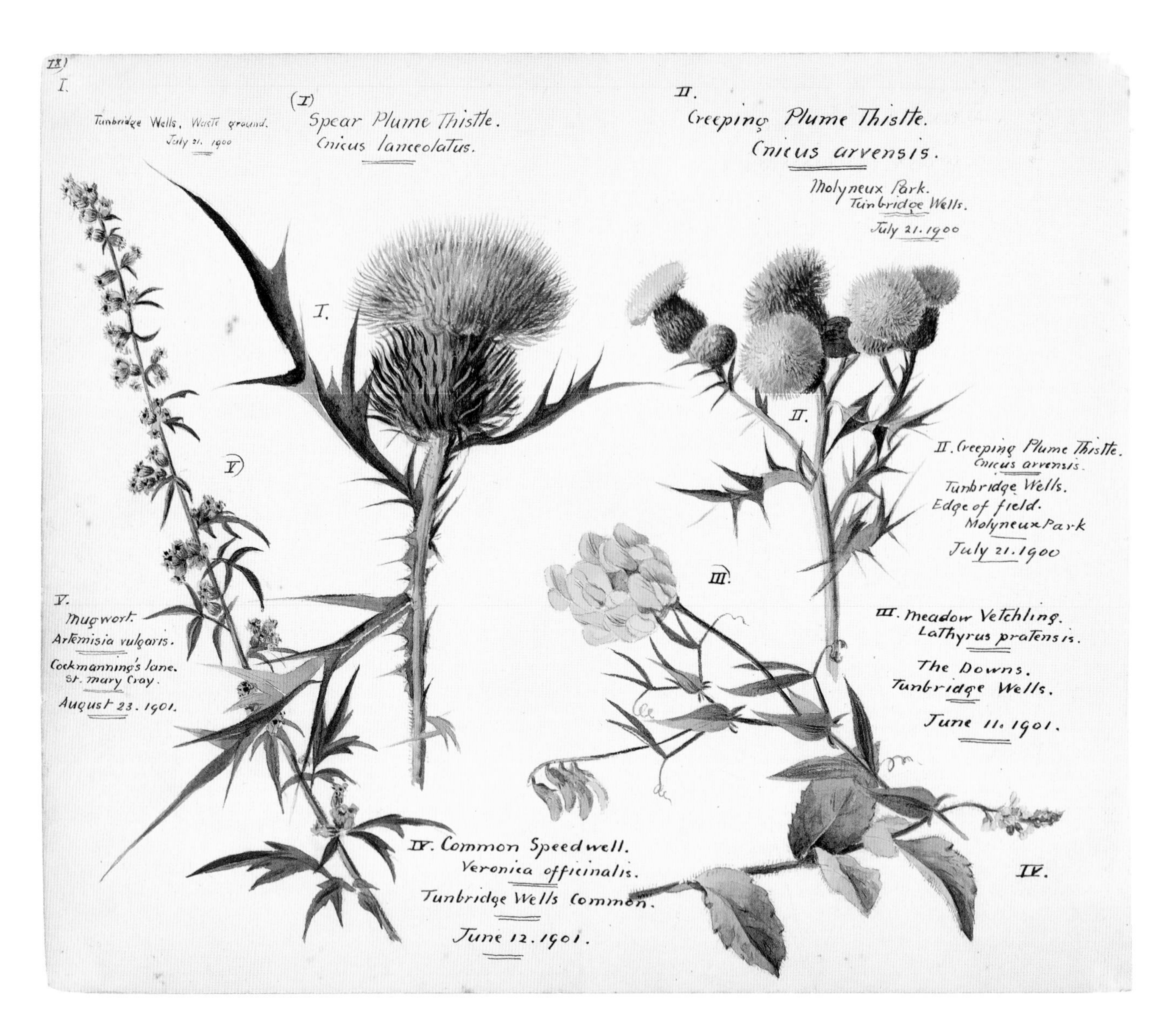
I.
Tunbridge Wells, Waste ground.
July 21. 1900
(I)
Spear Plume Thistle.
Cnicus lanceolatus.
II.
Creeping Plume Thistle.
Cnicus arvensis.
Molyneux Park.
Tunbridge Wells.
July 21. 1900
II. Creeping Plume Thistle.
Cnicus arvensis.
Tunbridge Wells.
Edge of field.
Molyneux Park
July 21. 1900
V.
Mugwort.
Artemisia vulgaris.
Cockmanning's lane.
St. Mary Cray.
August 23. 1901.
III. Meadow Vetchling.
Lathyrus pratensis.
The Downs.
Tunbridge Wells.
June 11. 1901.
IV. Common Speedwell.
Veronica officinalis.
Tunbridge Wells Common.
June 12. 1901.

Spear thistle, *Cirsium vulgare* (I); creeping thistle, *Cirsium arvense* (II); meadow vetchling, *Lathyrus pratensis* (III); heath speedwell, *Veronica officinalis* (IV); and mugwort, *Artemisia vulgaris* (V)

19

20

21

22

August

23

24

25

August
September

26

27

28

29

30

31

1

2

September

3

6

4

7

5

8

September

9

10

11

12

13

14

15

V.
III. Lesser Snapdragon.
Antirrhinum Orontium.
St Mary Cray. Cornfield.
August 3. 1901.
Downe. Kent.
August 20. 1901.
VI.
Basil Thyme.
Calamintha arvensis.
Chalky bank. Downe.
August 20.
1901.
I.
V.
VI.
II,
III.
II.
Sweet Violet.
Viola odoráta.
Chelsfield lane.
April 17. 1901.
(I)
marsh marigold.
Cáltha palústris.
Orpington Mill.
marshy ground
April 25. 1901.
IV.
IV. Cinquefoil.
Meadow Bank.
Tunbridge Wells.
July 14. 1901.

Marsh marigold or kingcup, *Caltha palustris* (I); sweet violet, *Viola odorata* (II); lesser snapdragon, *Misopates orontium* (III); double-flowered creeping cinquefoil, *Potentilla reptans* (IV); red hemp-nettle, *Galeopsis angustifolia* (V); and basil thyme, *Clinopodium acinos* (VI)

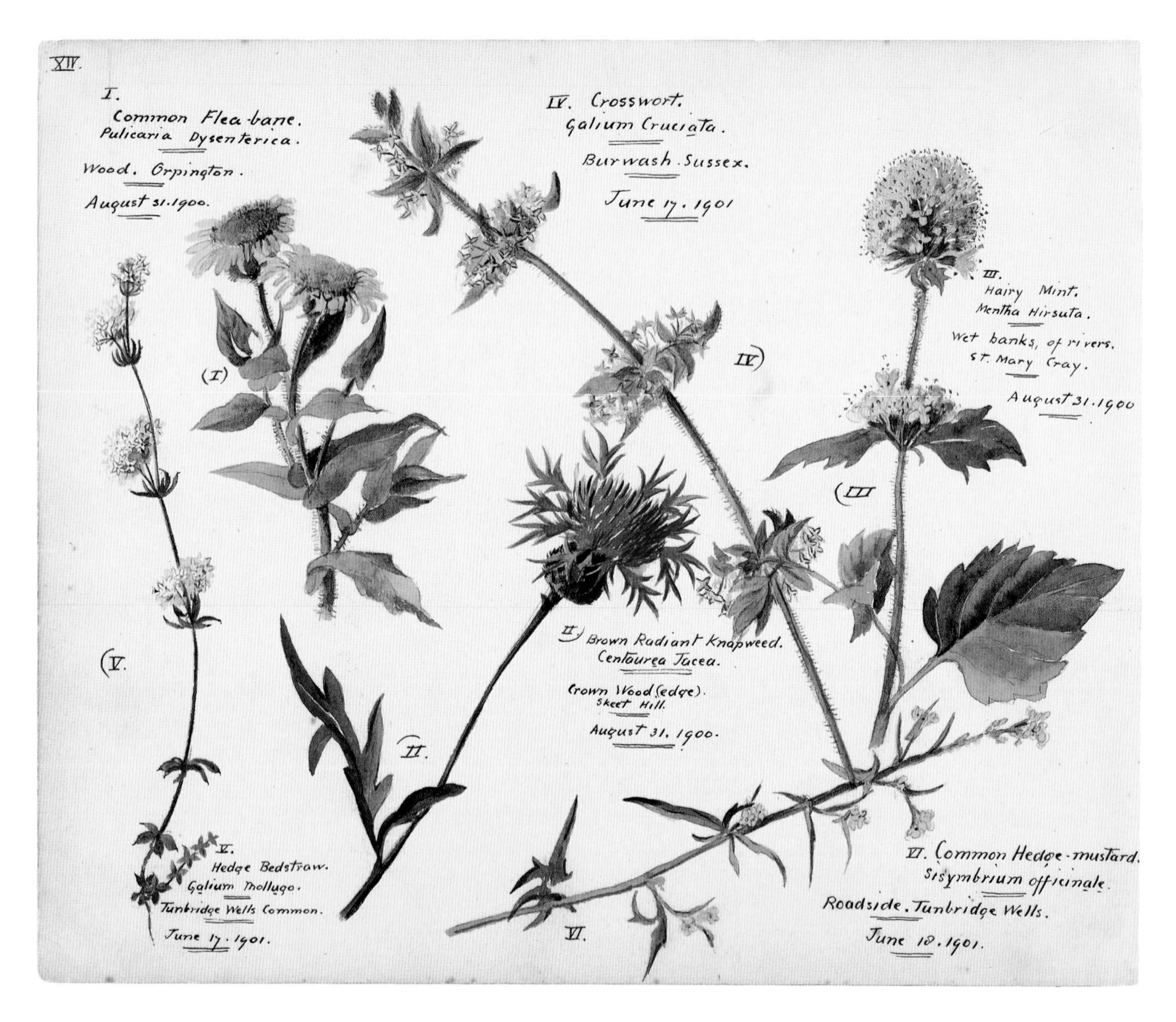
XIV.
I.
Common Flea-bane.
Pulicaria Dysenterica.
Wood. Orpington.
August 31. 1900.
IV. Crosswort.
Galium Cruciata.
Burwash. Sussex.
June 17. 1901
(I)
IV)
III. Hairy Mint.
Mentha Hirsuta.
Wet banks, of rivers.
St. Mary Cray.
August 31. 1900
(III
(V.
II. Brown Radiant Knapweed.
Centaurea Jacea.
Crown Wood (edge).
Skeet Hill.
August 31. 1900.
II.
V. Hedge Bedstraw.
Galium Mollugo.
Tunbridge Wells Common.
June 17. 1901.
VI.
VI. Common Hedge-mustard.
Sisymbrium officinale.
Roadside. Tunbridge Wells.
June 18. 1901.

Common fleabane, *Pulicaria dystenterica* (I); greater knapweed, *Centaurea scabiosa* (II); water mint, *Mentha aquatica* (III); crosswort, *Cruciata laevipes* (IV); hedge bedstraw, *Galium mollugo* (V); and hedge mustard, *Sisymbrium officinale* (VI)

16

17

18

19

September

20

21

22

September

23

24

25

26

27

28

29

September October

30

1

2

3

4

5

6

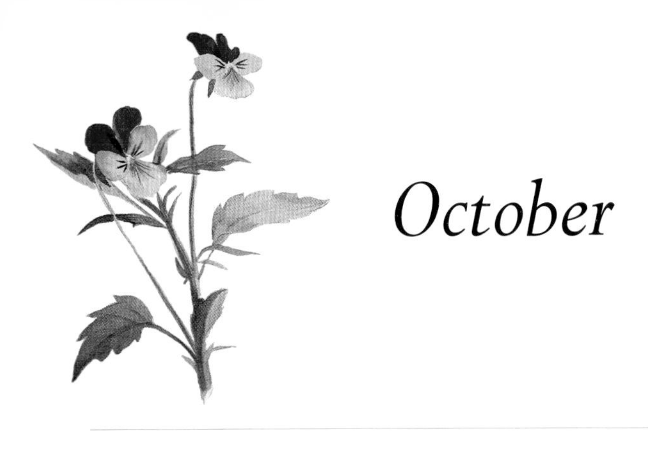

October

7

8

9

10

11

12

13

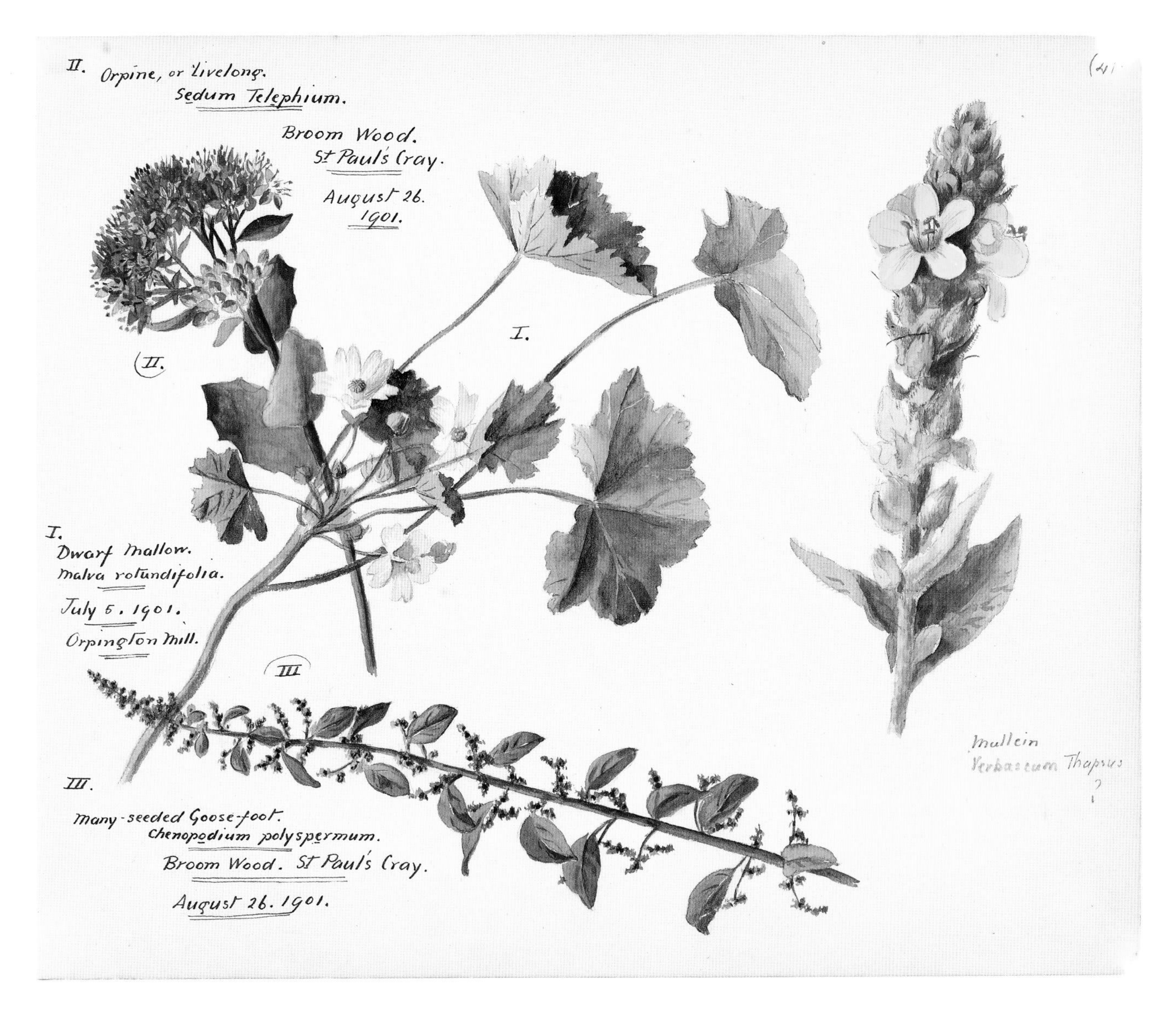
II. Orpine, or Livelong.
Sedum Telephium.
Broom Wood.
St Paul's Cray.
August 26.
1901.
I.
(II.
I.
Dwarf Mallow.
Malva rotundifolia.
July 5. 1901.
Orpington Mill.
III
III.
Many-seeded Goose-foot.
Chenopodium polyspermum.
Broom Wood. St Paul's Cray.
August 26. 1901.
Mullein
Verbascum Thapsus

Dwarf mallow, *Malva neglecta* (I); orpine, *Sedum telephium* (II); many-seeded goosefoot or allseed, *Chenopodium polyspermum* (III); and great mullein or Aaron's rod, *Verbascum thapsus* (right)

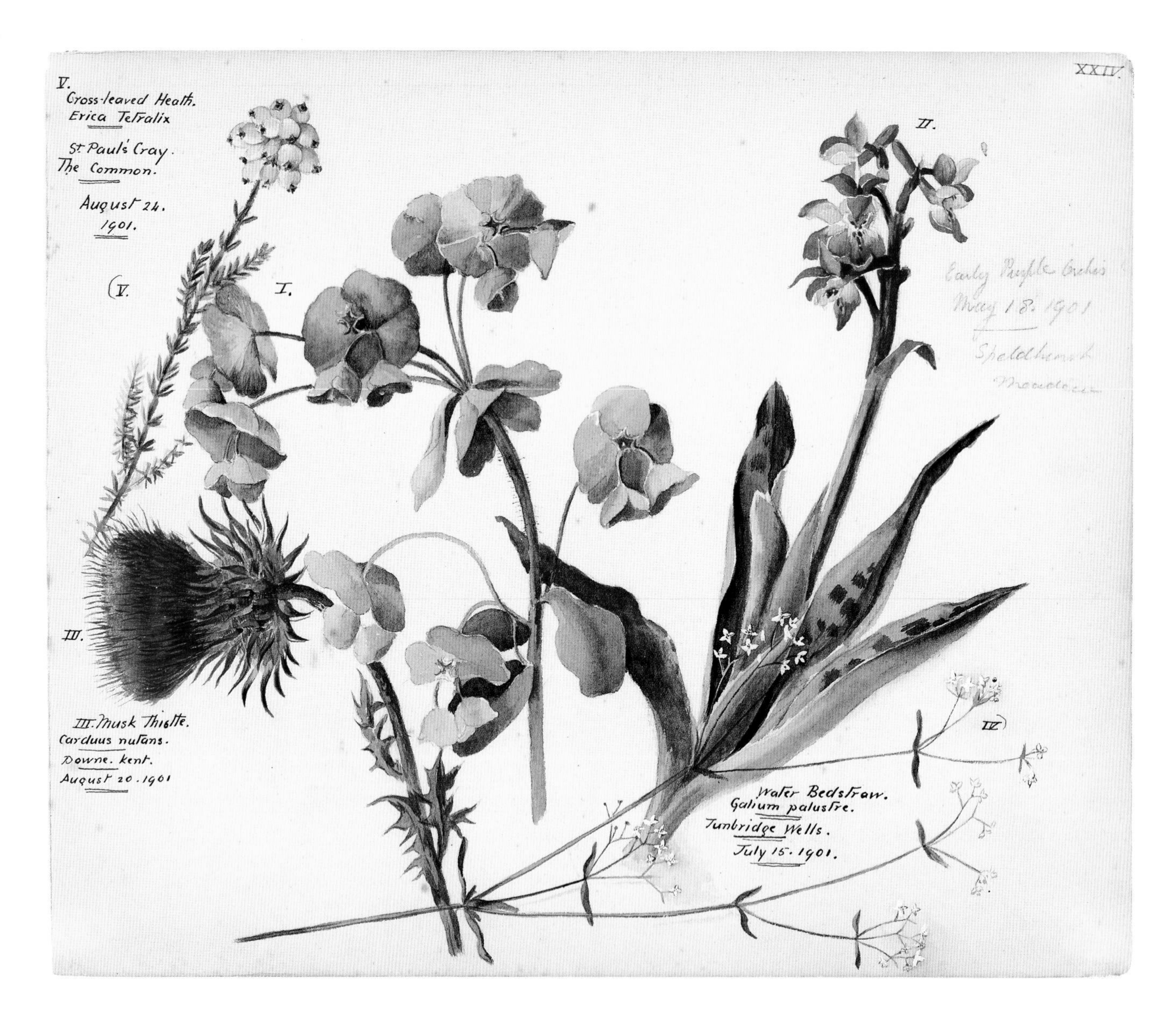
XXIV.
V.
Cross-leaved Heath.
Erica Tetralix
St. Paul's Cray.
The Common.
August 24.
1901.
(V.
I.
II.
Early Purple Orchis
May 18. 1901
III.
III. Musk Thistle.
Carduus nutans.
Downe. Kent.
August 20. 1901
IV)
Water Bedstraw.
Galium palustre.
Tunbridge Wells.
July 15. 1901.

Wood spurge, *Euphorbia amygdaloides* (I); early purple orchid, *Orchis mascula* (II); musk or nodding thistle, *Carduus nutans* (III); common marsh bedstraw, *Galium palustre* (IV); and cross-leaved heath, *Erica tetralix* (V)

14

15

16

17

October

18

19

20

October

24

21

25

22

26

23

27

28

29

30

31

October November

1

2

3

November

4

5

6

7

8

9

10

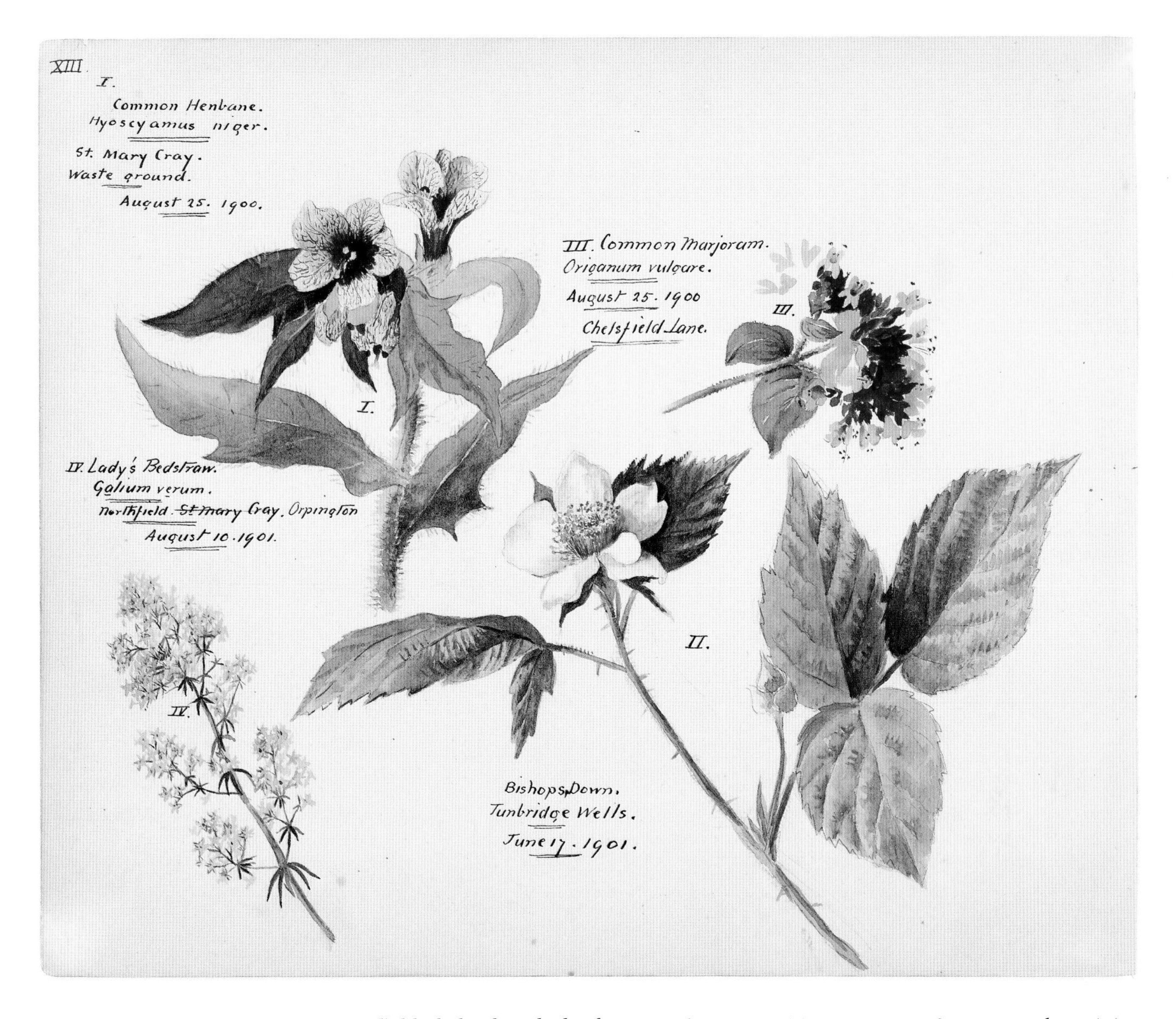
XIII
I.
Common Henbane.
Hyoscyamus niger.
St. Mary Cray.
Waste ground.
August 25. 1900.
III. Common Marjoram.
Origanum vulgare.
August 25. 1900
Chelsfield Lane.
III.
I.
IV. Lady's Bedstraw.
Galium verum.
Northfield. St Mary Cray. Orpington
August 10. 1901.
II.
IV.
Bishops Down.
Tunbridge Wells.
June 17. 1901.

Henbane, *Hyoscyamus niger* (I); probably hybrid with dewberry, *Rubus caesius* (II); marjoram, *Origanum vulgare* (III); and lady's bedstraw, *Galium verun* (IV)

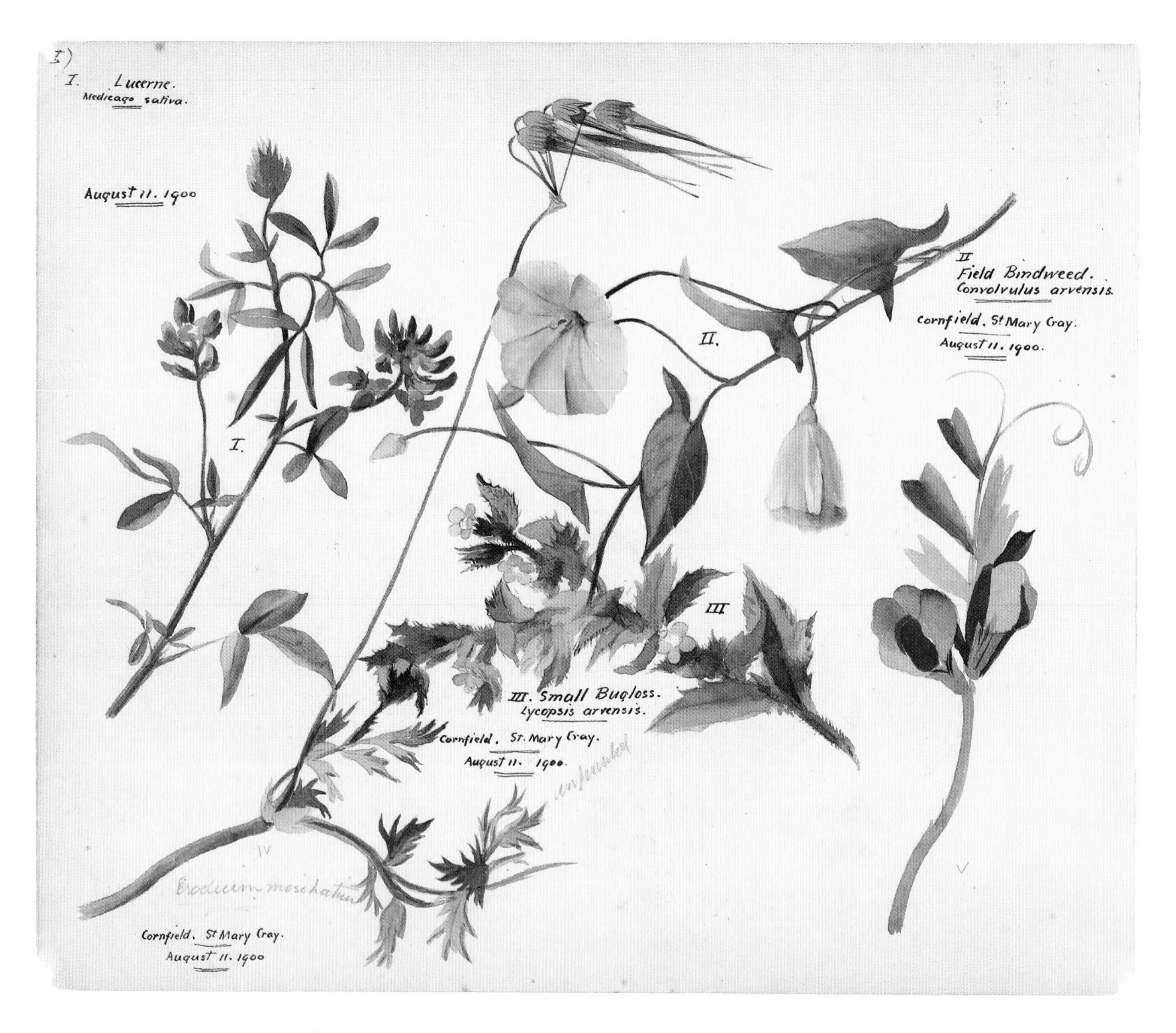
I. Lucerne.
Medicago sativa.
August 11. 1900
I.
II
Field Bindweed.
Convolvulus arvensis.
Cornfield. St Mary Cray.
August 11. 1900.
II.
III
III. Small Bugloss.
Lycopsis arvensis.
Cornfield. St. Mary Cray.
August 11. 1900.
IV
Erodium moschatum
Cornfield. St Mary Cray.
August 11. 1900
V

Lucerne, *Medicago sativa* (I); field bindweed, *Convolvulus arvensis* (II); small bugloss, *Lycopsis arvensis* (III); musk stork's bill, *Erodium moschatum* (IV); and common vetch, *Vicia sativa* ssp. *segetalis* (V)

11

November

12

15

13

16

14

17

November

18

19

20

21

22

23

24

25

26

27

28

November
December

29

30

1

December

2

3

4

5

6

7

8

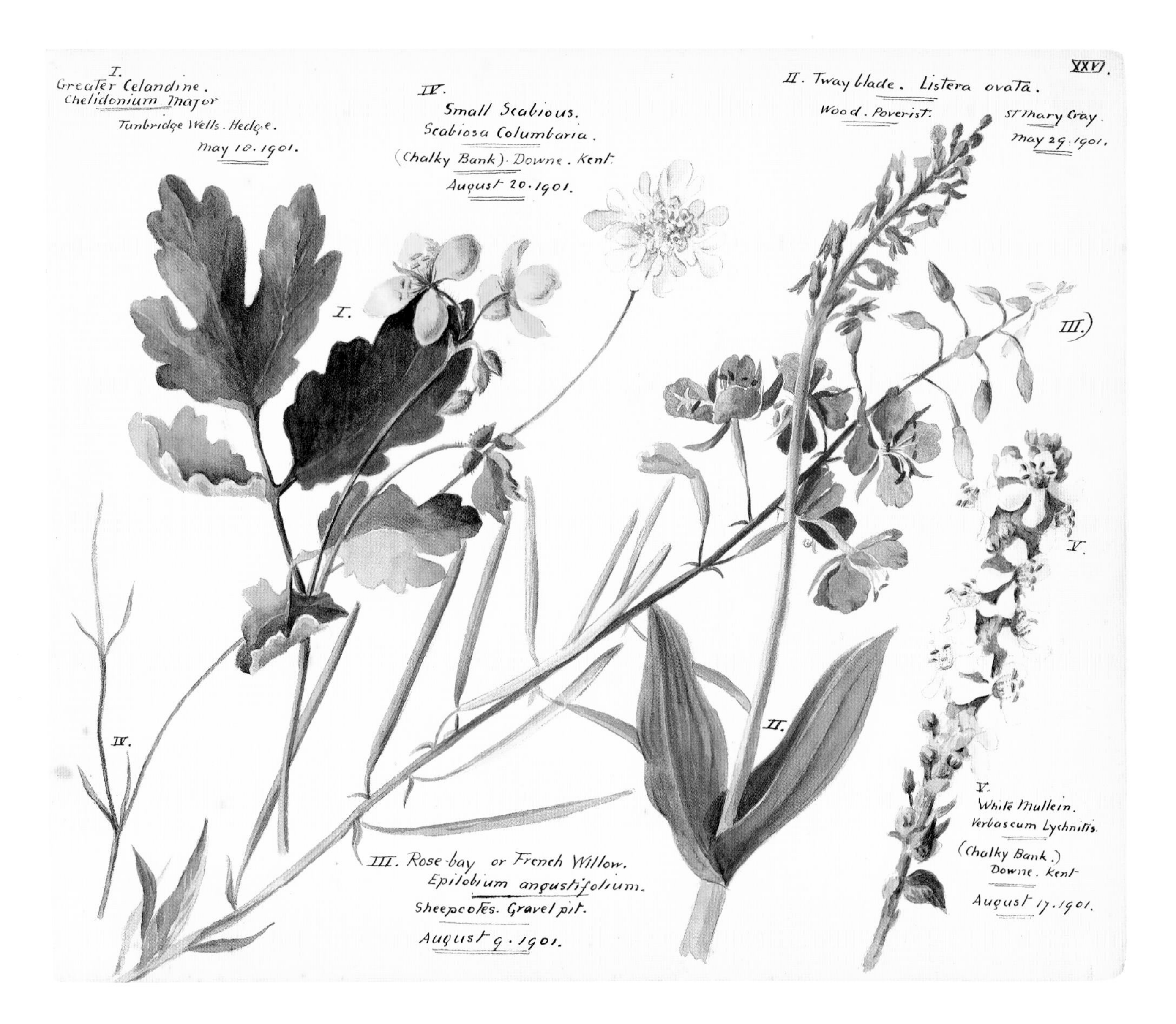
XXV.
I.
Greater Celandine.
Chelidonium Major
Tunbridge Wells. Hedge.
May 18. 1901.
IV.
Small Scabious.
Scabiosa Columbaria.
(Chalky Bank). Downe. Kent.
August 20. 1901.
II. Tway blade. Listera ovata.
Wood. Poverist.
St Mary Cray.
May 29. 1901.
I.
III.
V.
IV.
II.
III. Rose-bay or French Willow.
Epilobium angustifolium.
Sheepcotes. Gravel pit.
August 9. 1901.
V.
White Mullein.
Verbascum Lychnitis.
(Chalky Bank.)
Downe. Kent
August 17. 1901.

Greater celandine, *Chelidonium majus* (I); common twayblade, *Listera ovata* (II); rosebay willowherb, *Epilobium angustifolium* (III); small scabious, *Scabiosa columbaria* (IV); and white mullein, *Verbascum lychnitis* (V)

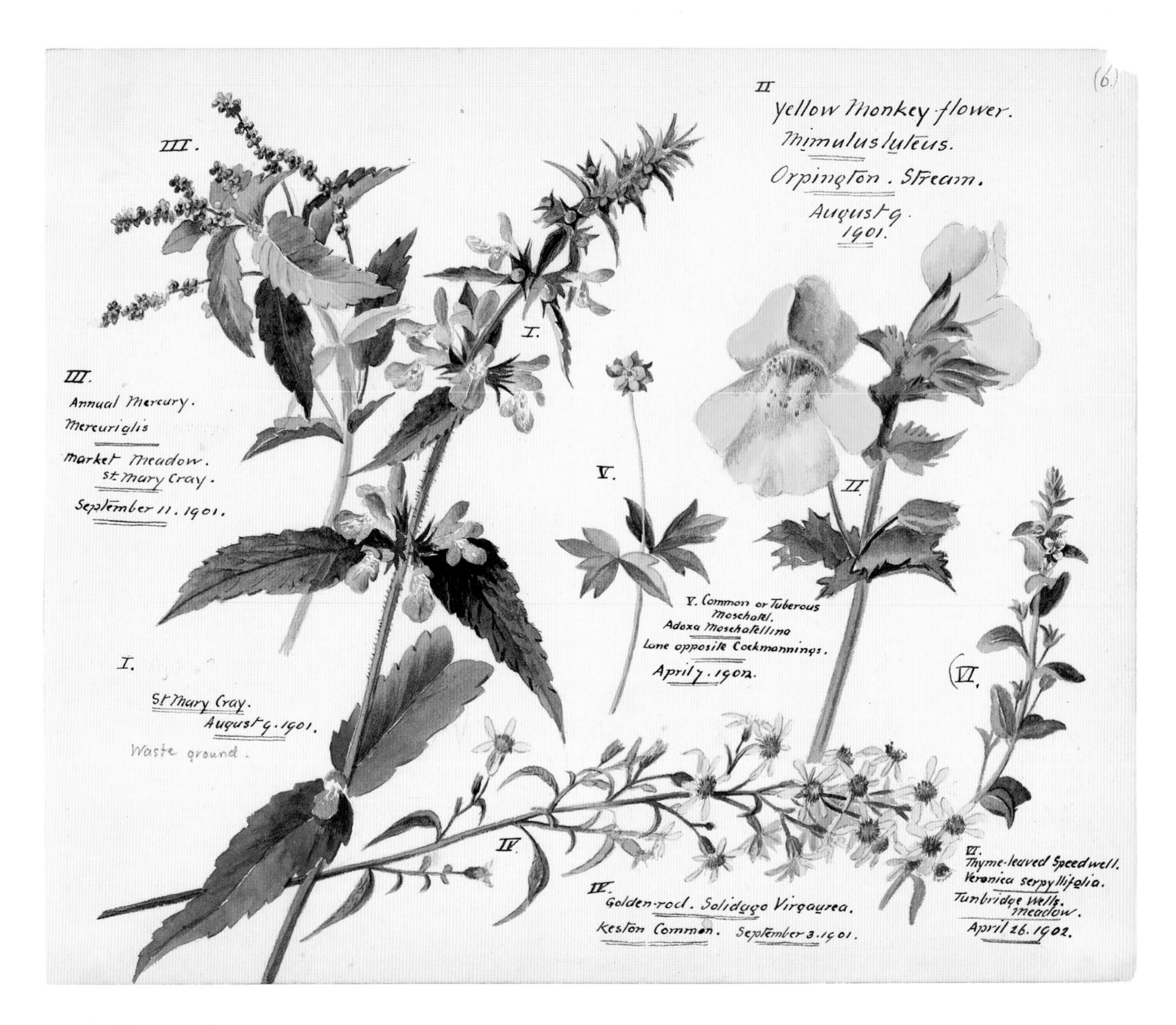
(6.)
II
Yellow Monkey-flower.
Mimulus luteus.
Orpington. Stream.
August 9.
1901.
III.
I.
III.
Annual Mercury.
Mercurialis
Market Meadow.
St Mary Cray.
September 11. 1901.
V.
II
V. Common or Tuberous
Moschatel.
Adoxa Moschatellina
Lane opposite Cockmannings.
April 7. 1902.
I.
St Mary Cray.
August 9. 1901.
Waste ground.
VI.
IV.
IV.
Golden-rod. Solidago Virgaurea.
Keston Common. September 3. 1901.
VI.
Thyme-leaved Speedwell.
Veronica serpyllifolia.
Tunbridge Wells.
meadow.
April 26. 1902.

Probably woundwort, *Stachys × ambigua* (I); monkey flower, *Mimulus guttatus* (II); annual mercury, *Mercuralis annua* (III); goldenrod, *Solidago virgaurea* (IV); moschatel or townhall clock, *Adoxa moschatellina* (V); and thyme-leaved speedwell, *Veronica serpyllifolia* (VI)

9

10

11

12

December

13

14

15

December

16

17

18

19

20

21

22

23

24

25

26

December

27

28

29

December

30

31

Notes

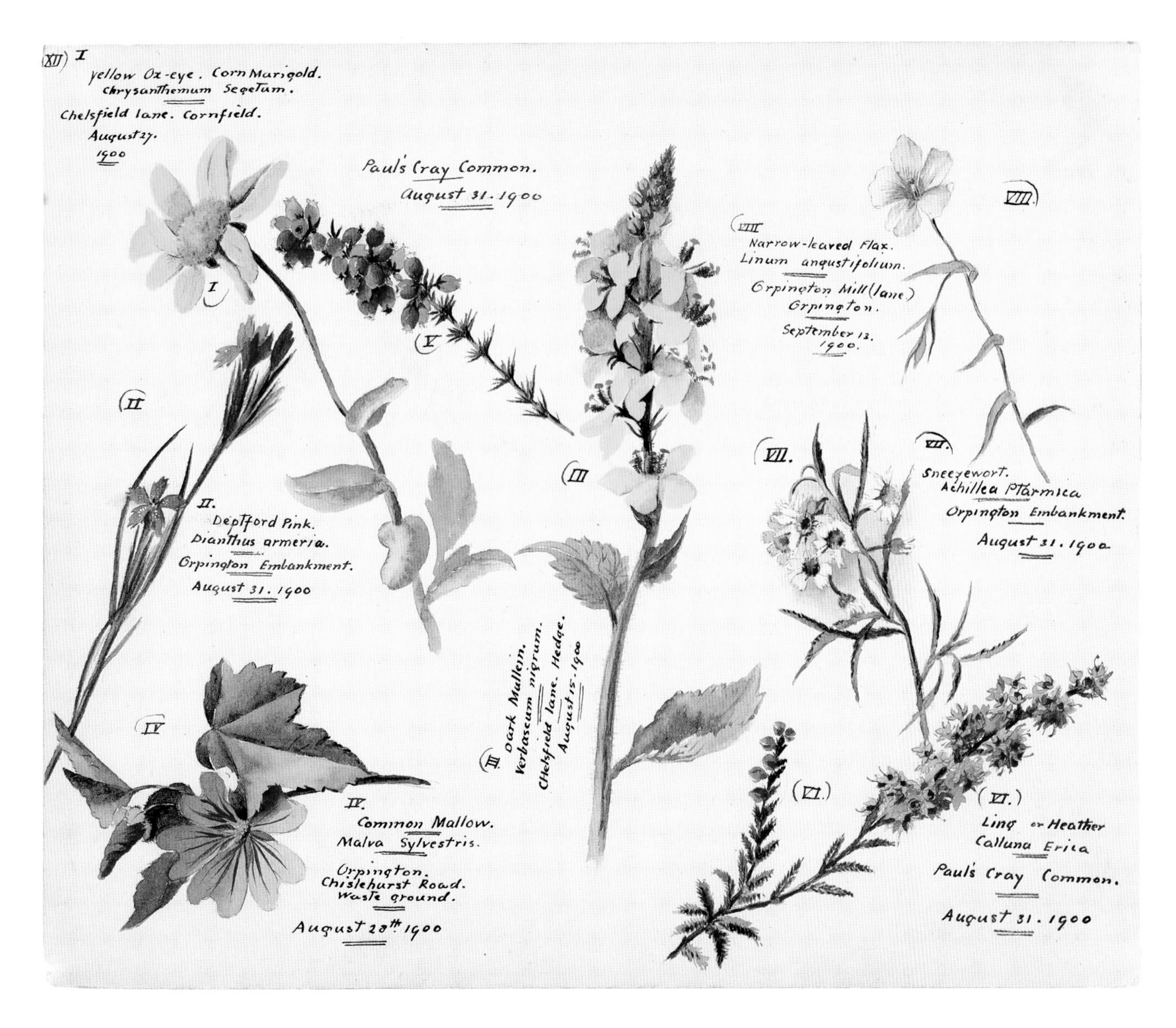

(XII) I
Yellow Ox-eye. Corn Marigold.
Chrysanthemum Segetum.
Chelsfield lane. Cornfield.
August 27.
1900
Paul's Cray Common.
August 31. 1900
VIII
Narrow-leaved Flax.
Linum angustifolium.
Orpington Mill (lane)
Orpington.
September 13.
1900.
VIII
I
V
II
II.
Deptford Pink.
Dianthus armeria.
Orpington Embankment.
August 31. 1900
III
VII.
VII.
Sneezewort.
Achillea Ptarmica
Orpington Embankment.
August 31. 1900
IV
III.
Dark Mullein.
Verbascum nigrum.
Chelsfield lane. Hedge.
August 15. 1900
IV.
Common Mallow.
Malva Sylvestris.
Orpington.
Chislehurst Road.
Waste ground.
August 28th 1900
VI.
VI.
Ling or Heather
Calluna Erica
Paul's Cray Common.
August 31. 1900

Corn marigold, *Chrysanthemum segetum* (I); Deptford pink, *Dianthus ameria* (II); dark mullein, *Verbascum nigrum* (III); common mallow, *Malva sylvestris* (IV); bell heather, *Erica cinerea* (V); heather or ling, *Calluna vulgaris* (VI); sneezewort, *Achillea ptarmica* (VII); and flax, *Linum usitatissimum* (VIII)

Notes